DESCRIPTIVE STATISTICS

B. Ritacca
Statistics.

DESCRIPTIVE STATISTICS

by

FREDA CONWAY

M.A. (COM.), B.Sc.

Lecturer in Statistics in the University of Leicester

LEICESTER UNIVERSITY PRESS

1963

Printed in The Netherlands by
Drukkerij Holland N.V., Amsterdam
for the Leicester University Press

ACKNOWLEDGEMENTS

Elementary text-books should not be original in their subject matter, though to justify their publication, they should present this information in a new way. The material for *Descriptive Statistics* has been gathered over a number of years from many books, articles, and lectures. I have acknowledged the sources of the statistical data that I have used, but these acknowledgements cover only a small part of my debt to these authors and teachers.

I am particularly grateful to the authors and publishers who have given me permission to quote their statistics. The majority of the statistical tables in this book have been derived from the publications of Her Majesty's Stationery Office and are reproduced by permission of the Controller. I am also indebted to the Royal Statistical Society, Basil Blackwell, the Times Publishing Co., and the Society of Medical Officers of Health for permission to quote from articles in journals published by them. I should also like to thank the United Nations for permission to use data from their *Demographic Year Book*: Basil Blackwell for permission to quote from H. F. Lydall's, *British Incomes and Savings*: Macmillan and Co., for permission to quote from Hartog and Rhodes' *Examination of Examinations*: Sir Ronald A. Fisher, Dr Frank Yates, and Oliver Boyd Ltd., for permission to abridge Table I from their book, *Statistical Tables for Biological, Agricultural and Medical Research*.

Lastly I wish to thank the Board of the Leicester University Press, their artist and printers, and the members of the administrative staff of the University who have assisted in the process of publication.

F. C.

The University
Leicester

CONTENTS

PART I

SOCIAL MEASUREMENTS

CHAPTER I

STATISTICS AND POLITICAL ARITHMETIC

T HE chief collectors of economic and social statistics are governments. These statistics are needed both as records and as guides to policy in the everyday business of administration. The quantity and quality of a government's statistics are a good indication of the range of its interests and its efficiency. The British government's activities cover almost every aspect of the lives of its citizens and its statistical records do the same. Not all these statistics are published, but many are available in official journals and reports. A glance at the *Annual Abstract of Statistics* is sufficient to show the variety of this information. The main headings include climate, population, health, education, crime, manpower, industrial production, transport, overseas trade, prices, wages, salaries, spending, and saving.

But it is not only central governments which collect and publish statistics; local authorities, international organizations, nationalized industries, trade associations and research organizations all add to the quantity published each year.

The collection of statistics is a relatively modern development. The keeping of various social records, including records of births and deaths, goods imported and exported was well established in Tudor England, but it was not until the seventeenth century that any of these records were used to prepare regular statistics.

In the late sixteenth and early seventeenth centuries London suffered from a number of plagues: mortality rates which were usually high, rose considerably at these times and one result of these recurring crises was the publication of the Bills of Mortality for the City of London and certain neighbouring parishes. These bills which gave information concerning both christenings and burials and attempted to distinguish between deaths from the plague and other deaths, were studied by John Graunt (1620–1674). He used them to estimate the total population of London and the effect of the plague on this population. Together with William Petty (1623–1687) he founded a new study to which Petty gave the name of Political Arithmetic. This was later described as "the art of reasoning by figures upon things relating to government," a description which fits much of the work that is done in social and economic statistics today.

It was however a long time before Political Arithmetic could develop into social statistics, since the governments of the seventeenth and eighteenth centuries collected relatively few numerical data. The collection and publication of social statistics involves a very considerable expenditure of time and money: it could only be undertaken as governments and other organizations became convinced of the need for this type of information.

During the second half of the seventeenth century there were several attempts to determine the balance of foreign trade: but the records of imports and exports were not kept in such a form as to make this an easy matter. Before the end of the century, however, the need for trade statistics was emphasized by the economic difficulties caused by the wars with France. In 1696 an Inspector General of Exports and Imports was appointed; it was his duty to prepare regular statistics for the use of the government.

In the eighteenth century there was considerable interest in estimates of the total population of the country, but the first census of population was not taken until 1801. By this time, the rapid growth of the population was the cause of much public concern as it was feared that further increases in total numbers might lead to famine and disaster. The growth of the insurance business in the same century fostered an interest in Life Tables, though it was not until civil registration of births and deaths was introduced in 1837, that satisfactory statistics became available for their construction.

In the nineteenth century the study of statistics became popular. During the first half of the century, statistical societies were started in a number of large towns. Only two of these societies now survive: the Manchester Statistical Society which was begun in 1833 and the London, now the Royal Statistical Society which was formed in the following year. Many members of these societies combined an interest in statistics with an interest in social reform. To them, statistics was a powerful tool with which to achieve their aims. Their attitude may be illustrated by brief accounts of the work of Dr William Farr and Charles Booth.

Dr Farr entered the General Register Office in 1839, about two years after it had been formed, and for the next forty years he supervised the collection of the vital statistics for England and Wales. Naturally he was interested in the prevention of disease and the promotion of public health and he used the collection and analysis of statistics to further these ends. In particular, he used the mortality rates for a selection of healthy districts as a standard against which to measure the defects of other localities and so provide an indication of the areas in which sanitary reform was most necessary.

Charles Booth was a Liverpool shipowner who moved to London in 1875 to open a branch office for his firm. At that time, London was regarded as one of the richest cities in the world, nevertheless it was obvious that many of its citizens lived in extreme poverty. For persons with a social conscience, poverty was the most serious social problem of the time, but no-one knew what should or could be done to improve the situation. Workmen wanted better wages, but did not know how to get them. Some employers agreed that wages were too low, but were unwilling to increase them unless their competitors did the same. The charity organizations attempted to solve the problem with private charity, but there were many who believed that charity sapped the independence of the poor and so made the situation worse, not better. In a paper to the London Statistical Society in 1887, Charles Booth remarked on this sense of helplessness, and suggested that before any social problem can be solved, it must be clearly stated, and if possible it should be expressed in numerical terms. It was this conviction which caused him to begin his survey of London Life and Labour the previous year.

This enquiry was started in two districts of the East End of London, the Tower Hamlets and the Hackney School Board Division. Its purpose was to determine the numbers of persons and families living in different degrees of poverty and at the same time to ascertain the chief causes of poverty. Charles Booth decided that the facts he required were all known to somebody: school-board officers, rent collectors, sanitary inspectors, relieving officers, ministers of religion and many other workers visited these families in the course of their duties. These officials were therefore interviewed by Charles Booth or one of his secretaries, and their evidence was used to classify each family according to the degree of poverty or comfort in which they lived. This enquiry was so successful that it was extended, with some modifications to the whole of London.

Charles Booth's conclusion that thirty per cent of the population of London were living in poverty was a shock to many people, including members of the government. Also by measuring both the extent and causes of poverty, the survey pointed the way to various methods of reducing it. Schemes were introduced for old age pensions and health insurance: trade boards were set up to regulate wages in some of the worst paid industries: labour exchanges were opened to help men and women find work. These reforms necessarily took several years to accomplish, but the work of Charles Booth helped to give direction to the movement for social reform which was so prominent a feature of the early years of the twentieth century.

In this century government participation in economic affairs has greatly increased, and the need for reliable and up to date statistics as an aid to the formulation of government economic policy is now widely recognized. The Statistics of Trade Act, 1947 gave the government additional powers for the collection of economic statistics and since that date there have been many developments and improvements in this field. The Census of Production has been re-organized and a Census of Distribution taken for the first time in this country. The indices of retail and wholesale prices have been revised and extended. At the same time, the work of different government departments has been co-ordinated so that their various statistics can be combined to give the estimates of National Income and Expenditure which are used to summarise changes in the economic condition of the country. A great deal has been achieved since 1947, and further developments have been planned; but continued improvement of economic statistics is essential if the government is to be in a position to meet its responsibility for ensuring the economic health of the country.

Social and economic statistics involve more than the collection of data. These data must be organized and presented in a suitable form before their significance can be appreciated. Petty and Graunt had to rely on fairly simple arithmetic to assist their reasoning, but social scientists today are able to use a great variety of analytical techniques.

Some of these techniques have been developed especially for use in the social sciences: certain forms of graphical representation, index numbers and the elementary analysis of time series are little used outside these sciences. But statistical methods as a whole are not unique to the social sciences: many of the techniques used by social scientists were first developed by workers in the natural and applied sciences, or by mathematicians whose primary interest has been in statistical theory.

Nevertheless, the purpose of social statistics is essentially the same as that of Political Arithmetic—"to reason by figures upon things relating to government." Its first concern must be the measurement of social phenomena and this involves consideration of the nature of the things to be measured and the accuracy of the measurements made as well as problems of statistical method.

For students of the social sciences there is another practical difficulty. Unlike the natural scientist they can only occasionally make their own observations or experiments. Generally they are dependent on others for the data with which they work. This means that they must learn where to find the statistical information they require, and how to assess its usefulness for their specific purposes as well as how to analyse it and present it efficiently.

Recommended Reading

Tippett, L. C. H. *Statistics*, Oxford University Press, 2nd Edition, 1956.

Kendall, M. G. 'The Statistical Approach', *Economica*, 1949. (Reprinted in *Readings in Market Research*, Ed: F. E. Edwards, British Market Research Bureau, 1956).

Clarke, G. N. *Science and Social Welfare in the Age of Newton*, The Clarendon Press, Oxford 1937.

Webb, B. *My Apprenticeship*, Longmans Green, 1926.

Simey, T. S. and Simey, M. B. *Charles Booth: Social Scientist*, Oxford University Press, 1960.

Little, I. M. D. 'The Economist in Whitehall'. *Lloyds Bank Review* April 1957.

Greenwood, M. *Medical Statistics from Graunt to Farr*. Cambridge University Press, 1948.

CHAPTER 2

DEFINITIONS FOR STATISTICS

IT is often suggested that one of the difficulties facing students
of the social sciences is the lack of a specialised vocabulary. Social
phenomena are every-day occurrences: consequently words such
as wages, income, sickness and employment which are used somewhat loosely in ordinary conversation must be given a precise
meaning before any attempt can be made to measure the things
that they describe.

Consider the question "What is the population of London?"
Before it can be answered, the words 'population' and 'London'
must be defined. Any other town could be substituted for London:
the same considerations would apply in all cases, though their relative
importance would vary very much with local circumstances.

A town may be regarded as an administrative unit, an economic
or social unit or as a continuously built-up area. Though in the case
of an ideal town all three definitions might give the same geographical
area, for all existing towns they would give different, possibly very
different, results.

The population of an area can also be defined in several ways.
The most usual definition is that of resident population. This seems
reasonable enough: summer visitors would not be regarded as part of
the population of a holiday resort, though for some purposes the total
of residents and visitors might be more useful than that of residents
alone. But the term "resident population" is not self-explanatory and
so is not precise enough for statistical purposes. Should it for example,
include school children, or students who are living away from home?

Since towns may be regarded as economic as well as residential
units, the population of a town might also be defined as the number
of persons who work in the industries of the town, together with
their dependents.

In practice, the choice of definition must depend on both the purpose for which the statistics are required and the kind of information
available. Population statistics are most easily obtained from census
data: it is therefore necessary to consider the kinds of estimate of town

populations which are given or can be made from census reports, and the relevance of these estimates to other definitions of town populations.

Census data are generally available for administrative areas, i.e. county and municipal boroughs and urban and rural districts. There is, therefore, no difficulty in obtaining an estimate of the population of a town which is defined as an administrative unit. If it is desired to define the town as an economic unit or as a continuously built up area it will be necessary to determine the administrative unit or units which approximate most closely to this definition. Some population statistics are available for parishes and in these cases there is a wider choice of town boundary.

The 1951 Census reports give three types of population estimate for each local authority area. These are described as the enumerated, resident and day populations respectively and are derived from answers to questions concerning the address at which each person is enumerated, their usual place of residence, and their place of work, if any.

The enumerated population of an area consists of all persons "living and counted" in the area at midnight on the day of the census.

The resident population of an area may be defined as consisting of all persons who normally live in the area for more than six months of each year. School children at boarding school and students resident at college are part of the resident population of the area in which the school or college is situated. The estimated resident population given in census reports is obtained by adjusting the enumerated population to allow for persons absent from their usual place of residence on census night. This resident population can also be adjusted to allow for the net movement to work into or out of the area to give a day-time population.

From a social or economic point of view, the resident and day populations are more significant than the enumerated population, but the latter has the advantage of greater accuracy. Questions relating to place of work and usual residence are not always answered correctly and residents who are absent from the country on census nights cannot be included in the estimates.*

* At the 1961 Census, the 10 per cent sample schedules included questions concerning absent members of households. This defect may therefore be remedied in the future.

For several centuries the City of London has been the centre of a relatively well populated area: consequently London has always been given special treatment by the collectors of statistics. The Bills of Mortality which were first published in 1592 covered a number of parishes outside the city itself. After 1603, when publication of the bills became regular, information for the City of Westminster was also included. In the first census report for 1801, statistics were given for the Metropolis, a rather larger area than that covered by the Bills of Mortality. The term Greater London was first used in the 1881 census: it was used to describe the Metropolitan Police District, an area slightly larger than the Metropolis. The boundaries of Greater London were slightly modified by the Police Act of 1946 and today this area is also known as the London Conurbation. The boundaries of the County of London were fixed by the London Government Act of 1899: this area is much smaller than the conurbation.

Census reports give statistics for each of these areas, the City, County, and conurbation of London. Table 2.1. shows three types of population estimate for each of them. Here then are nine estimates of the population of London: in this case the choice of geographical area is much more important than the type of population estimate used. There is very little difference between the enumerated and resident populations of these areas. The difference between the resident and day populations is very large for the city, but is not so important for either the County or Greater London.

It would of course be possible to define London in terms of larger or smaller areas for special purposes such as problems of transport or town planning.

TABLE 2.1
THE POPULATION OF LONDON, 1951

Area	Enumerated Population	Resident Population (000's)	Day Population
City	5·3	5·2	340
County	3,348	3,353	4,177
Conurbation	8,348	8,348	8,520

Source: Census 1951, England and Wales. Report on Usual Residence and Workplace.

The results obtained for London are typical of those which could be obtained for other conurbations. It may however be noted that for self-contained towns, the day and resident populations would be identical, but dormitory areas have a larger resident population and workplaces a larger day population. The differences between enumerated and resident populations are usually small, but holiday resorts tend to have larger enumerated populations and industrial towns larger resident populations.

Housing statistics provide another example of the need for precise definitions. Statistics of housing are also included in the population census reports though the kind of information published has varied considerably in the last one hundred and fifty years.

At the first census in 1801, the enumerators were asked to give the number of houses in their districts, but they were not given a definition of a house. Generally it is easy to know whether a building is a house or not, but there are some cases e.g. colleges, inns of court and tenement houses in which it is necessary to decide whether a building should count as one or many houses. This problem was recognized, but was regarded as too difficult to allow of a general solution. The enumerators were therefore allowed to make their own decisions in these cases, with the result that different practices were adopted in different districts. The problem was particularly serious in Scotland which had large numbers of houses divided into flats: in Edinburgh only the houses were counted but in Glasgow each flat was counted as one house. In 1841 Edinburgh adopted the same method as Glasgow and the number of its houses showed a corresponding increase.

At the 1851 census, a house was defined as "all the space within the external or party walls of a building:" flats could no longer be counted as houses. This definition of a house was adopted by the International Statistical Conference in London in 1860 and was used at each census in England and Wales and Scotland up to and including 1911. But it was not a satisfactory definition, and additional questions were introduced concerning the size of houses. In 1891 information was obtained concerning the number of rooms in all houses with four rooms or less, and in 1911 a distinction was made between houses occupied by private families and those occupied by institutions: also a new definition, that of "separate dwellings" was used to distinguish between houses and flats. In 1921 this definition was clarified by the use of the term "structurally separate dwelling" which was and still is defined as "any room or suite of rooms intended or used for habitation having separate access to the street or to a common landing or staircase to which visitors have access."

It is worth noting that the formulation of suitable definitions for international comparisons may prove even more difficult than that of finding definitions for national statistics. The following note is taken from a report* of a United Nations committee of experts which was concerned with methods of comparing standards or levels of living in different countries. Housing conditions are an important aspect of the standard of living, but it is not easy to obtain suitable measurements for this purpose.

"One great difficulty is the definition of a house. A house may consist only of rooms or it may include enclosed open spaces: it may involve only accommodation for human beings or (as in a number of countries) also provide for domestic animals including cattle. It may be made of bricks, or earth or cement or even of thatched material. It may or may not use iron or glass or even timber. And in regard to the shape and form of the house there is such a diversity of national or sub-national factors involved such as environment, climate, availability of building materials, kinship system, composition of family and various local traditions and values, that it would seem almost impossible to devise any indicators that could give even a partial measure of the housing component in the levels of living even within a country, let alone for purposes of international comparison."

When using statistics, it is always important to check the definitions used in their collection: and this process of checking should be concerned with many aspects of the data.

The time and place to which the statistics relate should be noted. Estimates can be made for a particular point of time, or they may be aggregates for a period. The Ministry of Education publish the number of children on the school registers for a certain day each

* *Report on International Definition and Measurement of Standards and Levels of Living*, U.N. 1954.

year: the Registrar-General gives the number of births occurring in each quarter: the Ministry of Labour has used both methods for counting the number of persons registering as unemployed.

National data may be available for the United Kingdom which includes Northern Ireland or for Great Britain which does not. Local data may be given for administrative areas or for the variety of areas with or without fixed boundaries which are used by different services. For any large town, it is possible to obtain many kinds of statistics, such as the number of births and deaths, the number of persons attending evening classes, the number of private telephones in use and the number of persons unemployed, but these statistics will not necessarily relate to the same population. Statistics of births and deaths relate to the resident populations of administrative areas, but people from outside the town may attend evening classes at the technical college, or register as unemployed at the Local Office of the Ministry of Labour: and telephone exchange districts do not necessarily coincide with local authority areas.

If the problem involves the use of statistics which have been collected for different times or places, it will be necessary to consider whether the same definitions have been used throughout. This is particularly important in the case of administrative statistics.

Though many statistics are collected by direct inquiries such as the census of population, many more are obtained in the course of the administration of government and industry. Such statistics are required in the first place for administrative purposes and the definitions used in their collection are influenced by administrative requirements. Statistics of the size of classes in schools relate to the number of pupils on each register and not necessarily to the numbers taught together by their teachers: definitions of personal income are largely dependent on the practices of Inland Revenue: statistics of imports and exports are influenced by customs regulations. Changes in administrative practice will normally involve changes in the methods used in the collection of such statistics and so affect the comparability of the information for different times and places.

Unemployment statistics have always been derived from the registration of unemployed persons applying for jobs. The earliest records were kept by Trade Unions and related to their own members. Since the introduction of unemployment insurance in 1912, the Government has collected its own statistics. Under the original scheme only 2–3 million workers were eligible for insurance. The scheme has been extended many times and today the number of insured employees is about 20 million. The local offices of the Ministry of Labour, formerly known as Labour Exchanges, have frequently been used by persons who wanted work but could not claim benefit. Nevertheless the possibility of drawing benefit has always been the most important incentive to registration and consequently the number of unemployed persons registering at these offices has reflected changes in the insurance scheme as well as changes in the unemployment situation.

Local variations in statistics may be partly due to differences in local administration. Criminal statistics, for example, reflect many factors as well as local variations in the incidence of crime. They are influenced by the efficiency and strength of the local police force, their methods of recording events and their willingness to prosecute in certain types of cases. The statistics are also influenced by the willingness of the public to report crimes and to co-operate with the police. All these factors must be kept in mind when comparisons are being made between different police districts.

Although a great many statistics are published today, the user of statistics often finds that the particular information he requires is not available. He may need to know the number of crimes committed but can only find the number known to the police: he may need to know the number of children attending school, but can only find the number of children on the school registers: he may need an estimate of the population of a built-up area centred on a particular town, but can only find the population for a number of administrative areas, which do not add exactly to the area he requires. This list could be extended indefinitely.

In some cases the user of statistics may decide that the difference in definition is unimportant for the purpose for which he requires the figures—for most localities the enumerated population provides a satisfactory estimate of the resident population at the same date. In other cases it will be necessary to use analytical methods to adjust the original data, and so make them more suitable for specific needs.

There are no general rules for dealing with problems of this kind: each case must be considered on its own merits. It must however be emphasized that failure to recognize relevant differences in the definitions of the available statistics and those required for a particular analysis can lead to serious mistakes.

This type of difficulty is illustrated in the following brief account of the Northampton Life Table.

Life Tables may be described as calculations designed to show how long the average man or woman of a particular age may be expected to live. Such tables are of obvious interest to insurance companies and should be calculated from information relating to the number of deaths and the number of persons living at each age. Today tables of this kind are published annually by the Registrar-General and the average expectation of life at birth is 67. 85 years for males and 73.53 years for females.* The Northampton Life Table was published by Dr Price in 1783. At that time the average expectation of life at birth was probably less than 30 years.

Since Dr Price was working before the first census of population was taken, he had no information concerning the numbers and ages of the population of Northampton. His only source of statistics was the Parish Register for All Saints for the years 1735–1780. As the register showed that the number of christenings was approximately the same as the number of burials during these years, Dr Price concluded that the population of the parish was more or less stationary. Unfortunately for his calculations, this conclusion was not correct. The burials were a fairly complete record of the deaths in the parish, but the christenings under-estimated the number of births, since there were many Baptists in this parish and their children were not christened. Also there was some migration from the country to the town during these years. The population of All Saints was not stationary as Dr Price assumed, but was growing fairly steadily. Consequently his calculations over-estimated the rate at which people were dying and under-estimated the time they could be expected to live.

Dr Price's Life Table was used by the Equitable Insurance Company. This company insured lives and the inaccuracy of the table increased

* *Registrar General's Statistical Review*, 1958.

their profits, since people lived to pay more premiums than was expected from the table. It was later used by the government for the sale of annuities: unfortunately this same error cost the government a great deal of money before it was realized that the table was at fault.

RECOMMENDED READING

Payne S. L. *The Art of Asking Questions,*
Studies in Public Opinion 3. Princeton University Press, 1951.
Carr-Saunders, A. M., Caradog-Jones, D., and Moser C. A.
A survey of social conditions in England and Wales illustrated by Statistics. The Clarendon Press, 1958.
Monthly Digest of Statistics Supplement: Definitions and Explanatory Notes H. M. S. O. (annually).

CHAPTER 3

THE PRESENTATION OF STATISTICS

A LITTLE consideration shows that any number, particularly any large number, means very little by itself. For example, the enumerated population of England and Wales at the 1951 Census was 43,757,888 persons. In order that this number can have a meaning, it must be compared with other related totals and it is convenient to round off these totals to the nearest thousand or even the nearest million to make them more readily understandable. In this case the population of England and Wales may be compared with the population of other countries at the same date. In 1951, the population of Scotland was approximately 5 million and that of Northern Ireland, 2 million, making a total of 51 million for the United Kingdom: the population of the United States was 154 million, that of France 42 million and that of Russia 193 million.

Since a single statistic is generally of little value, it is necessary to consider the best means of presenting the statistics required on any occasion. If only a few figures are wanted, they can easily be inserted into a verbal description. If many figures are needed, it is more convenient to present them in tables. In some cases the relationships between the figures will be obvious, in others it will be desirable to bring out these relationships by the calculation of further statistics or the use of diagrams.

There are many ways of analysing the relationships between quantities, but the simplest comparisons that can be made between data of the same kind involve consideration of either absolute or proportionate differences. It is possible to consider how much larger one quantity is than another or how many times larger one quantity is than another. The former comparison only involves subtraction: the latter involves the use of rates, ratios or percentages.

These two types of comparison may give very different results. During the intercensal period 1931–1951, the population of Corby increased by 947 per cent, that of Leicester by only 11 per cent. But Corby was a very small place in 1931 and this 947 per cent represented an additional 15,000 persons: Leicester was and is a fairly large city and the increase of 11 per cent in its population meant an additional 27,000 persons. The absolute change in population was greater for Leicester than for Corby, but the rate of change was very much less.

To some extent rates, ratios and percentages are interchangeable, though custom and convenience often determine which method is used in a particular case. Unemployment is measured as a percentage: the number of unemployed is expressed as a percentage of the total, employed and unemployed. The proportion of a population dying in a year is expressed as a rate: the death rate is the number of deaths during the year per 1,000 living at the middle of the year. Ratios are usually only used when the required values are whole numbers or simple fractions. Since such values rarely occur in practice, rates and percentages are used much more frequently than ratios. Nevertheless approximate ratios are often useful. For instance the data for the populations quoted at the beginning of this chapter can be expressed in this form. The population of the United Kingdom is about one third that of the United States, or about one quarter that of Russia.

When interpreting percentages or ratios it is important to remember that both these measurements are fractions and the value of a fraction depends on both its numerator and denominator. Changes in either or both of these quantities will affect the value of the ratio or percentage. Company dividends and the measurement of absenteeism in industry provide useful illustrations of this point.

In assessing the profitability of a company over a period of time it is necessary to consider changes in the issued capital as well as changes in declared dividends, since the latter are generally expressed as a percentage of the former. Suppose a company with an issued capital of 500,000 shares of £1 each, finds that its net assets have increased to £1,000,000 and that it is in a position to distribute an annual dividend of £50,000. If it decides to leave its issued capital unchanged, it will declare a dividend of 10 per cent: but if it decides to issue 500,000 bonus shares, so that its issued capital is increased to £ 1,000,000 it will declare a dividend of only 5 per cent: the amount of dividend received by the shareholders will be the same in both cases.

In industry absence rates are usually obtained by expressing the time lost as a percentage of the time that might have been worked.

This method is satisfactory if the working week or working year for which the rates are calculated is kept constant, since under these circumstances a reduction in absenteeism is equivalent to an increase in the time worked. But changes in the normal working time involve changes in the rate of absenteeism even if the time worked is unaltered. An absence rate of two days out of five (40 per cent) is higher than a rate of one day out of four (25 per cent) even though the number of days worked is the same in both cases.

It is often convenient to express percentages in the form of index numbers: e.g. the fact that the population of Leicester increased by 11 per cent in the period 1931 to 1951 might be written in this way.

$$\text{Index of Population 1951 (1931} = 100) = 111.$$

This form of comparison is particularly useful for a series of values and allows for both increases and decreases to be shown without the use of plus and minus signs. An example is given in Table 3.1.

TABLE 3.1
CHANGES IN TOWN POPULATIONS

Year	Resident population (000's)		Index Numbers (1931 = 100)	
	Liverpool CB.	Oxford CB.	Liverpool CB.	Oxford CB.
1931	856	81	100	100
1939	822	96	96	119
1948	793	106	93	131
1951	785	107	92	132

Source of data: Census 1951, England and Wales: Report on Usual Residence and Workplace.

Percentages should not be used to hide the fact that the samples on which they are based are small. Schools have been known to advertise 100 per cent examination successes without mentioning the fact that they only presented one or two candidates for the examination: but such advertisements are hardly likely to improve their reputations.

In some cases it will be useful to illustrate the statistics by means of diagrams.

There are three main methods of representing quantities diagrammatically. They may be represented by lengths, areas, or by repeated symbols. These methods may be used singly or in combination and there are many ways of elaborating them in practice.

The first of these methods is illustrated in Diagram 3.1. A involves the use of a series of straight lines with lengths proportional to the quantities being represented. In B, these lines are replaced by rectangles of equal width: this type of diagram is known as a bar-chart. In C, the quantities are represented by points on a graph whose distances from the x-axis are proportional to the quantities being represented.

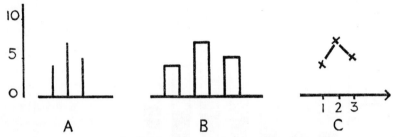

DIAGRAM 3.1. *In each of these diagrams, the quantities represented are 4, 7, and 5 units respectively.*

Bar charts are particularly easy to construct and are suitable for many kinds of data. Histograms and population pyramids are special types of bar-chart: they will be considered later. Graphs are particularly useful for time series, and a combination of graphs and bar-charts is often used to give annual data for several years together with monthly data for recent months. Both graphs and bar charts can be used to compare either absolute or relative values, and bar charts are often used to show the composition of aggregates.

Examples of bar-charts and graphs are given in Diagrams 3.2 and 3.4.

The bar charts of Diagram 3.2. show some aspects of the variation in household expenditure with changes of income. The first set of diagrams shows actual expenditure in shillings per week for two person households. Only four categories of goods and services are distinguished: food; housing, fuel and light; clothing and footwear; and other items. Expenditure on each of these groups tends to increase with increases in income, though as the second set of diagrams which have been drawn from percentages make clear, the increase in expenditure on these groups is not necessarily proportional to the increase

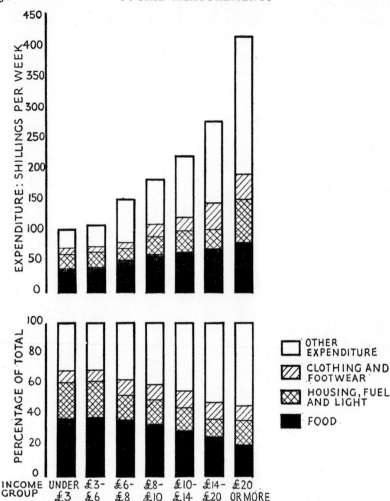

DIAGRAM 3.2. *Household Expenditure, U.K. 1953–54*

Expenditure of two-person households grouped according to total gross income of household.
Source of data: Report of Enquiry into Household Expenditure
1953–54, H.M.S.O. 1957.

in income. Generally the higher income groups allocate a smaller proportion of their total expenditure to food and fuel and light and housing, than do the lower income groups. The fact that in this survey, households with incomes of £3—£6 per week allocated a slightly higher proportion of their total expenditure to food than those with incomes under £3 per week may be accounted for by the fact that the latter group was mainly composed of "old-age pensioners" whose set of priorities may well differ from those of the rest of the population.

Graphs may be drawn on either ordinary or logarithmic (ratio) scales. The former are used for comparisons of absolute differences, the latter for comparisons of proportionate differences.

When graphs are drawn on ordinary scales equal changes in the variable are represented by equal distances along the y-axis and lines with the same slope indicate equal absolute changes in a given period of time. On logarithmic scales, lines with the same slope indicate equal rates of change. This type of scale can easily be understood by considering a ratio scale in units of 2 as shown in Diagram 3.3. This particular scale would be inconvenient in practice. It is more usual to use a logarithmic scale, i.e. a ratio scale with units of 10. This can be done either by plotting the actual quantities on semi-logarithmic graph paper, or by plotting the logarithms of the quantities on ordinary graph paper.

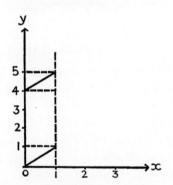 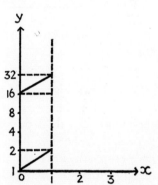

DIAGRAM 3.3. *Ordinary and Ratio Scales.*

A. Ordinary Scale: the line showing an increase from 0 to 1 has the same slope as line showing an increase from 4 to 5. In both cases the absolute increase is 1 unit.

B. Ratio Scale: the line showing an increase from 1 to 2 has the same slope as the line showing an increase from 16 to 32. In both cases the value of *y* is doubled.

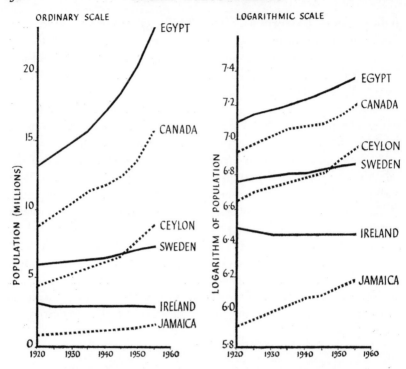

DIAGRAM 3.4. *Population Growth in Various Countries.*
Source of data: U.N. Demographic Year Book

The use of these two types of graph is illustrated in Diagram 3.4. which shows changes in the total population of six fairly small countries for the years 1920 to 1955. From both graphs it is clear that while the total population of Ireland declined slightly in this period, the other five countries have gained population. The ordinary scale emphasizes that the absolute gain in population has been greater in Egypt than in any of the other four countries, but Egypt also has the largest of these populations. The logarithmic scale graph shows that the most rapid rates of increase have occurred in Ceylon and Jamaica.

　Though the areas used to represent quantities in diagrams may be of any shape, it is most usual to use circles or semi-circles. Like bar-charts these diagrams can be divided to show the composition of aggregates. They have one important advantage over bar-charts:

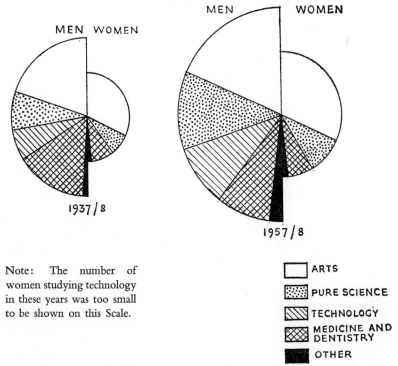

MEN WOMEN

1937/8

MEN WOMEN

1957/8

Note: The number of women studying technology in these years was too small to be shown on this Scale.

☐ ARTS

▦ PURE SCIENCE

▨ TECHNOLOGY

▧ MEDICINE AND DENTISTRY

■ OTHER

DIAGRAM 3.5. *University Students classified by Faculty, Great Britain 1937–8 and 1957–8.*

Source of data: Annual Abstract of Statistics

since the radii of the circles are proportional to the square roots of the original quantities instead of to the quantities themselves, they can be used to illustrate aggregates of very different values. Alternatively, by keeping the circles a constant size, it is possible to focus attention on changes in the composition of the aggregates.

Pie-diagrams, like bar-charts, should be constructed from cumulative data. In this case cumulative percentages are required: the angles at the centre may be obtained by determining the appropriate percentages of 180° or 360°; alternatively protractors are available which are graduated in percentages instead of degrees.

Diagram 3.5. uses pie-diagrams to compare the distribution of university students between faculties in a pre-war and a post-war

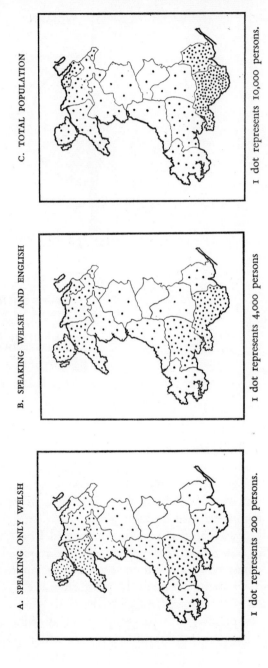

A. SPEAKING ONLY WELSH

B. SPEAKING WELSH AND ENGLISH

C. TOTAL POPULATION

1 dot represents 200 persons.

1 dot represents 4,000 persons

1 dot represents 10,000 persons.

DIAGRAM 3.6. *Geographical Distribution of the Welsh speaking Population of Wales, 1951.*

Data relate to population aged 3 years or more and have been taken from the Report of Welsh Speaking Population. Census 1951, England and Wales.

year. The number of students was very much greater in 1957/58 than it had been in 1937/38: but the proportion of arts students had not declined very much in spite of government and other propaganda for the promotion of scientific studies in the post-war years.

A third type of diagram involves the use of repeated symbols, each symbol representing the same quantity. This method can be used to give attractive diagrams for newspaper and magazine articles though it is not suitable for all types of data. Maps showing the distribution of population by plotting a series of dots, each representing so many persons, use a very simple form of this method. An example is given in Diagram 3.6. These maps show quite clearly that although the population of Wales is mainly concentrated in the south, the proportion of the population who speak Welsh is highest in the northern and western countries which are farthest from England.

Whatever type of diagram is used, the choice of scale is most important. When using bar-charts or graphs drawn on ordinary scales it is important to show the zero. Failure to do so exaggerates the differences between the dates, groups or localities for which the data are given. This can easily be seen by covering up a portion of the bar charts of Diagram 3.2. By starting at, say, 70s. per week and ignoring the divisions into types of expenditure it would be possible to suggest that the lowest income groups spent practically nothing and so to exaggerate the difference between these groups and the rest.

The choice of scales for a single time series is sometimes very difficult. In Diagram 3.7. the graph for the population of Egypt has been isolated from the other graphs of Diagram 3.4. and re-drawn on two different sets of scales. The first graph suggests a much greater rate of increase than the second, though both represent the same data. This does not mean that a single graph is useless: if such graphs are drawn for sufficiently long periods of time, or if they show values for relatively short intervals of time, they can be used to study the nature of the changes that have taken place in the period. Further discussion of this subject is included in Chapter 9.

In all the examples considered so far, comparisons have been made between quantities of the same kind. Many practical problems involve an analysis of the relationship between quantities of different kinds. When the data are given as time series it is often tempting to plot

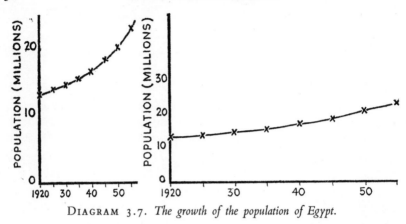

DIAGRAM 3.7. *The growth of the population of Egypt.*

them on the same diagram using two or more quite different scales. This is rarely satisfactory as the following example illustrates.

Diagram 3.8. shows changes in output and average earnings per manshift for face workers in the coal-mining industry. The first graph (A) suggests that during the years 1948–51 earnings and output changed at more or less the same rate, but that in the years 1951–58 earnings increased much faster than output. But how reliable is this conclusion? By changing the position and scale of the graphs it is possible to suggest very different conclusions. In Diagram B, the same scales have been used, but the position of the output scale has been changed: from this graph it appears that earnings have lagged behind output for the major part of the period shown. In Diagram C, the position of the scales is unchanged, but the scale for output has been doubled. This graph suggests that both output and earnings have increased rapidly.

It is impossible to come to any satisfactory conclusions from these graphs: what is needed is information concerning the relation between earnings and output. This can easily be calculated from the original data from which the graphs were drawn, and expressed in the form of earnings in shillings per hundred weight of mined coal. These figures would show that there has been an increase in the labour cost per hundred weight of mined coal, that this increase has mainly occurred since 1951 and was greatest in the years 1956 and 1957. Such an analysis might seem to justify the choice of Diagram A

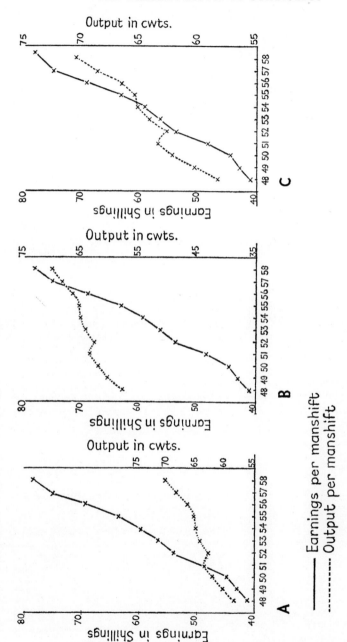

DIAGRAM 3.8. *Earnings and Output in the Coal Industry 1948–58*

Source of data: National Coal Board Report and Accounts.
N.B. Both sets of data relate to face-workers.

since it suggests some of the correct conclusions, even though the scales on which it is drawn are somewhat arbitrary.*

Lastly it is important to emphasize that diagrams should not be allowed to become too complicated. A complicated diagram is just as difficult to understand as a complicated statistical table, but whereas it is often possible to subject a table to further analysis, diagrams must be accepted or rejected at their face value.

* This example was suggested by a graph which was published in the Manchester Guardian for January 15, 1958 and the correspondence concerning it which was published later.

Recommended Reading

Buzzard, R. B. 'Attendance and Absence in Industry',
   British Journal of Sociology, 1954.
Huff, D. *How to lie with Statistics*, Gollancz, 1954.
Spear, M. E. *Charting Statistics*, McGraw-Hill, 1952.
'Contest in Curves', *The Economist*, Nov. 10, 1951.
'Charts for Every Occasion'. *The Economist*, Dec. 27, 1958.

CHAPTER 4

THE POPULATION OF ENGLAND AND WALES

WHEN the first population census for England and Wales was taken in 1801, the population numbered approximately nine million. At the time, the population was increasing rapidly and there was much public concern lest the growth of population should outstrip the increase in food production. This concern was expressed in the writings of Malthus and others and was an important factor in the decision to take the first census.

The population continued to grow rapidly: in the next fifty years it doubled itself. In the second half of the nineteenth century the rate of growth was not so rapid as it had been earlier, even so the population had reached thirty million by the end of the century. In this century the total population has continued to increase, though in the nineteen-twenties and thirties the rate of increase was very much reduced and many people became concerned lest this small rate of increase should turn into a decrease.

Calculations published in the thirties suggested that this decline might have begun by 1950. Today these fears appear exaggerated. The total population has not declined; indeed it is now expected to increase at least until the end of the century. At present there is more interest in the changes that are taking place in the age-sex composition of the population than there is in possible future changes in total numbers.

It is however both interesting and instructive to consider the circumstances which have caused such radical changes in public opinion.

The rate of growth of a population is determined by three factors: the number of births, the number of deaths and the balance of migration into or out of a country. For England and Wales as a whole, the numerical affect of migration has been small compared with the changes that have taken place in the number of births and deaths. The effect of migration need not, therefore, be considered at this stage of the discussion. Information concerning the total population, numbers of births and deaths, birth-rates and death-rates for

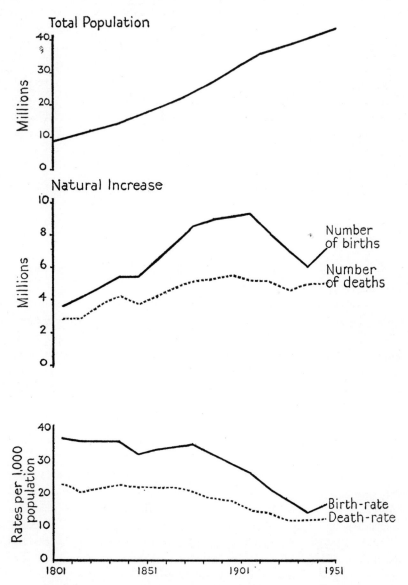

DIAGRAM 4.1. *The Population of England and Wales 1801–1951.*

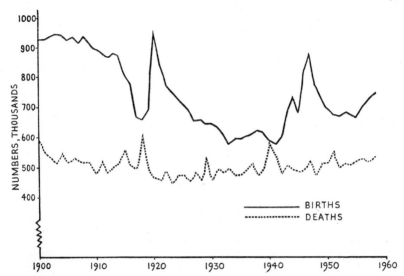

DIAGRAM 4.2. *Numbers of Births and Deaths: England and Wales 1900–1956.**
Source of data: Registrar-General's Statistical Review.

the period 1801–1951 is given in Table 4.1. and illustrated in Diagrams 4.1. and 4.2.

Throughout the whole of the nineteenth century the birth-rate and the death-rate were considerably higher than they are today, and the birth-rate was well above the death-rate so that the population was increasing fairly rapidly. During the latter part of the century there was a marked decline in both these rates and this decline continued in the present century. As the birth-rate fell more rapidly than the death-rate, particularly after 1911, the gap between these rates narrowed until in the nineteen thirties it varied around three per thousand. This difference is known as the rate of natural increase and in these years it seemed likely that this small rate of natural increase would turn into a rate of natural decrease.

The same conclusion could be reached by considering changes in the annual number of births and deaths. These numbers tended to increase throughout the whole of the nineteenth century though the number of births was considerably larger than the number of deaths. These increases in the numbers of births and deaths were, of course,

* War casualties abroad are not included in deaths.

TABLE 4.1

THE POPULATION OF ENGLAND AND WALES 1801–1951

Years	Census population at beginning of decade 000's	Inter-censal increase per cent	Number of births 000's	Number of deaths 000's	Birth rate per 1,000	Death rate per 1,000
1801–1810	8,893	14·00	3,675	2,808	37·5	23·9
1811–1820	10,164	18·06	4,140	2,894	36·6	21·1
1821–1830	12,000	15·80	4,798	3,547	36·6	22·6
1831–1840	13,897	14·27	5,505	4,225	36·6	23·4
1841–1850	15,914	12·65	5,489	3,769	32·6	22·4
1851–1860	17,928	11·90	6,472	4,211	34·1	22·2
1861–1870	20,066	13·21	7,500	4,794	35·2	22·5
1871–1880	22,712	14·36	8,589	5,178	35·4	21·4
1881–1890	25,974	11·65	8,890	5,244	32·4	19·1
1891–1900	29,003	12·17	9,155	5,575	29·9	18·2
1901–1910	32,528	10·89	9,298	5,249	27·2	15·4
1911–1920	36,070	4·93	8,096	5,188	21·8	14·4
1921–1930	37,887	5·53	7,129	4,723	18·3	12·1
1931–1940	39,952 ⎱ 4·67		6,065	4,992	14·9	12·3
1941–1950	* 41,748 ⎰		7,251	4,998	16·9	12·4
1951–	43,758					

* Mid-year estimate.

Sources: Census 1951, England and Wales. General Report.
Registrar General's Statistical Review 1951.
Brownlee. J. History of the birth-rates and death-rates in England
and Wales. Public Health June–July 1916.

consistent with declining birth-rates and death-rates since the total
population was increasing. If the effect of the 1914–18 war is ignored,
the average annual number of births declined fairly rapidly from
about 1905. The number of deaths declined more slowly, but this
decline had begun a little earlier and the number of deaths reached a
minimum in the twenties. By the thirties the difference between the
number of births and deaths was relatively small, and whereas it
seemed likely that the number of births would continue to decline, it
seemed reasonable to assume that the number of deaths would increase.

Changes in the rate of growth of a population are normally
accompanied by changes in its age structure and these in turn affect

the rate of future growth. By the nineteen-thirties, it appeared likely that these demographic factors would also depress the rate of natural increase still further.

Information concerning the age-structure of the population, at various dates, is given in Table 4.2. and illustrated in the population pyramids of Diagram 4.3. These are simplified pyramids; it is usual to show males and females separately and to use five-year age groups, but some of this detail has been omitted here in order that the data for several years might be shown on one diagram.

In 1871, the birth-rate and the death-rate were both high, but the birth-rate was slightly higher than the death-rate and the population was increasing and had been increasing for a very considerable time. This population had a high proportion of children and young adults and the pyramid representing its age structure is a triangle. Each rectangle is larger than the one above which represents an older age-group. This is partly because the younger age-groups were survivors of larger numbers of births and partly because there had been fewer deaths among them. The pyramid for 1851, which is not shown here, has the same characteristics as that for 1871.

Improvements in mortality rates and a decline in the birth-rate, both tend to round off the pyramid, since both tend to equalize the numbers in successive age groups. The pyramids for 1891 and 1911

TABLE 4.2
THE POPULATION OF ENGLAND AND WALES 1851–1951

| Age-distributions | | | | | | Thousands |
Age	1851	1871	1891	1911	1931	1951
0–10	4,441	5,778	6,949	7,551	6,313	6,880
10–20	3,671	4,605	6,175	6,836	6,642	5,516
20–30	3,137	3,785	4,997	6,255	6,852	6,207
30–40	2,365	2,901	3,809	5,490	5,858	6,402
40–50	1,768	2,283	2,884	4,158	5,218	6,537
50–60	1,235	1,663	2,044	2,881	4,450	5,248
60–70	809	1,064	1,345	1,827	2,928	3,972
70–80	396	506	651	864	1,371	2,352
80 & over	107	128	149	208	322	644
All ages	17,928	22,712	29,003	36,070	39,952	43,758

Census 1951, England and Wales, General Tables.

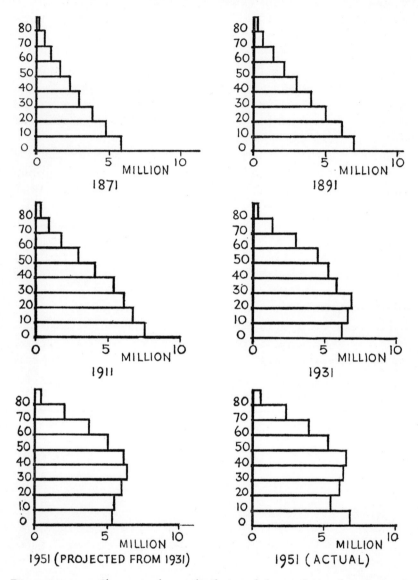

DIAGRAM 4.3. *Changes in the age-distribution of the population of England and Wales.*

illustrate two stages of this development. By 1931, the fall in the birth-rate had gone so far as to reduce the numbers in the youngest age-groups: this is clearly seen in the pyramid for that year which shows a "bulge" in the 20–30 age group. Also by 1931, the proportion of persons over sixty years of age had increased considerably.

Diagram 4.2. also includes a pyramid for the population of 1951 as it might have been anticipated or projected from the conditions of 1931, and this pyramid may be compared with that drawn from 1951 Census data.

The method employed in making such projections can easily be understood by considering the derivation of one diagram from the other. Since all persons aged 20 years or more in 1951 were alive in 1931, the rectangles representing these age groups in the 1951 pyramid can be obtained by moving the rectangles of the 1931 pyramid up two places and shortening them to allow for the deaths that could have been expected in the intervening years. Two new rectangles are then introduced at the bottom of the pyramid to represent the survivors of those to be born during the same twenty years.

The methods adopted for this projection are very rough, but the assumptions on which it is based are assumptions which would have been considered reasonable in the nineteen-thirties. At that time it seemed likely that as the proportion of elderly persons in the population increased, the death-rate would also increase. Also it was clear that the rapid fall in the birth-rate was largely due to a reduction in the average size of families, since the proportion of young adults (ages 20–40) had not changed very much in the first thirty years of this century. If this trend towards small families continued, the number of children in succeeding generations would become progressively less.

Reasonable or not, these assumptions have not been justified by events: the projected pyramid differs in important respects from that derived from actual data for 1951: in other words, this projection would have been of no value as a forecast!

During the years 1931–1951, the all age death-rate has shown considerable annual variations but has shown no tendency to increase. The projection over-estimates the number of deaths that have occurred in this period; but this error is not so serious as its underestimation of the number of births. The birth-rate has also varied greatly during these twenty years, but it was higher in 1951 than in 1931 and was particularly high in the immediate post-war years 1946–48. Some part of the difference between the actual and projected populations may be explained by the effects of the second world war, but this is only a partial explanation.

Changes in birth rates and death rates are influenced by many social and economic factors: some, such as wars and economic depressions, must be regarded as producing short term variations: others which include technical progress affect the long term trend. Any change in the rate of growth of the population inevitably affects its age-sex structure and so produces secondary effects in its rate of growth some years later.

The fall in the death rate which occurred in the last century and has continued in this century has been due to improvements in medicine, in the sanitary conditions of towns and in standards of living. The famine and disaster prophesied by Malthus has not occurred: but economic progress has been much greater than anyone could have foreseen at the beginning of the nineteenth century.

Changes in the birth rate may also have been induced by social and economic factors, though in this case it is more difficult to establish a causal relationship. Certainly as standards of living have risen the cost of bringing up children has increased very considerably, and this fact may have caused many parents to limit the size of their families. In this century, there have been increased opportunities for women to obtain employment outside the home and this change in the economic status of women may also have encouraged the trend to smaller families. The fall in infant and child mortality rates may have had a similar effect: as these improved, it was no longer necessary to have a large family to ensure the survival of one adult son or daughter. The increase in knowledge of contraception, and the acceptance of its practice by a growing number of persons, no doubt helped many parents to achieve the smaller families that they desired.

But if these factors explain the fall in the birth rate before 1935, their continued existence can hardly explain the higher birth rates of the nineteen fifties. There are, however, some important differences between these two periods.

Whereas the early nineteen-thirties were a period of unemployment and economic depression, the post-war years have been a period of full employment. Economic prosperity has encouraged both earlier marriage and a higher birth rate. Demographic changes have also tended to produce the same result. In 1931 women formed 52·2 per cent of the population of ages 15 to 45 years and 52·0 per cent of the population ages 20 to 35. By 1951 these percentages had been reduced to 50·8 and 50·9 respectively. Although more boys are born than girls, their mortality rates are higher at all ages, and this reduces the proportion of males in the adult population. In the nineteen-twenties and thirties this proportion was further reduced by the casualties of the 1914-18 war and by the migration to America, Canada and Australia which occurred before and after World War I and which affected young men much more than young women. World War II caused many fewer casualties: migration took place in both directions, and many women migrated to America and elsewhere as the wives of allied servicemen. Incidentally it may be noted that this change in the sex ratio is likely to be permanent. There has been a very great reduction in infant mortality in this century and this has resulted in more boys surviving childhood. The same factors which have reduced the infant mortality rate have also tended to increase the proportion of boys born.

Also it is possible that there has been a change in public opinion concerning the desirable size of families. The parents of the early years of this century had themselves been children in large families. They were aware of all the disadvantages that these entailed, such as the sharing of limited and often inadequate resources, and the immense burdens placed on the mother of such a family. It would only be natural if these parents wished to avoid these disadvantages and so decided to limit their own families to one or two children. But twenty to forty years later, the children of these small families are themselves parents, and being aware of the disadvantages of small families, particularly the loneliness of only children, may well have decided in favour of slightly larger families for themselves.

It is clear from this discussion that it is not easy to anticipate the future: most of the population projections made in the past have proved false. Nevertheless estimates of future populations are frequently needed for the formulation of economic and social policy. Perhaps it is only necessary to mention two obvious examples. The high birth rates of the years 1947–50 have caused considerable difficulties for educational authorities, as the "bulge" has passed through the schools. Also in devising schemes for retirement or old-age pensions it is necessary to be able to estimate the number of persons who will require them.

The general method of making population projections has been indicated in the discussion of the pyramid for the projected population of 1951. For a country such as England and Wales, for which mortality rates are low and can only be expected to change slowly, but birth rates are more variable, projections of the number of persons of pensionable age are likely to be more accurate than projections of the numbers of children of school age, and the more distant the projection, the less reliable it is likely to prove.

Estimates of the Population of England and Wales for the years 1978, and 1998 are given in Table 4.3. These projections are based on the estimated population for 1958, and have been taken from the Registrar-General's Statistical Review for that year. They suggest that the total population will continue to grow slowly for the rest of the century: and that by the end of the century there will be a rather higher proportion of persons of pensionable age, and a rather lower proportion of children under fifteen years of age than there are today. The proportion of persons of working age is unlikely to change very much.

This discussion of population changes in England and Wales can be useful in another way. There are obvious similarities in the demographic development of all countries: a study of the demographic history of any one country is therefore relevant to an understanding of the demographic problems of many others.

The demographic development of many Western European countries has involved three distinct stages. Initially these populations had high birth rates and high death rates, both of which were subject to considerable annual variations. In this period, the rate of natural increase was slow, and in some years the population declined. During the second stage, both the birth-rate and the death-rate declined from these high levels: in these countries, the death-rate declined earlier

TABLE 4.3

POPULATION PROJECTIONS FOR ENGLAND AND WALES

Age Groups	1958 Actual	1978 Projected	1998 Projected
	Thousands		
0–10	6,725	7,339	7,709
10–20	6,476	7,111	7,500
20–30	5,764	6,668	7,290
30–40	6,407	6,395	7,046
40–50	6,293	5,624	6,546
50–60	5,960	5,981	6,051
60–70	4,226	5,162	4,720
70–80	2,553	3,544	3,667
80 and over	840	1,169	1,494
Total	45,244	48,993	52,023
	Percentages		
Children 0–15	22·8	22·3	22·1
Workers M 15–65 *F* 15–60	62·6	60·0	61·2
Pensioners M 65+ *F* 60+	14·6	17·7	16·7

Source: Registrar General's Statistical Review, 1958.

and more rapidly than the birth-rate, consequently the second stage was a period of rapidly increasing populations. In the third and present stage, both the birth-rate and death-rate appear to be stabilised at fairly low levels. In this stage, the rate of natural increase is small, and varies from one year to the next.

Many African and Asian populations are only at the beginning of the second stage; their death rates have fallen considerably in recent years, but their birth-rates have fallen little or not at all. If their development follows the Western pattern, such countries must expect very large increases in population before they can hope to reach stability. Diagram 4.4. illustrates some population statistics for France and Japan, two countries which are at different stages of demographic development.

So far there has been little mention of migration in this discussion:

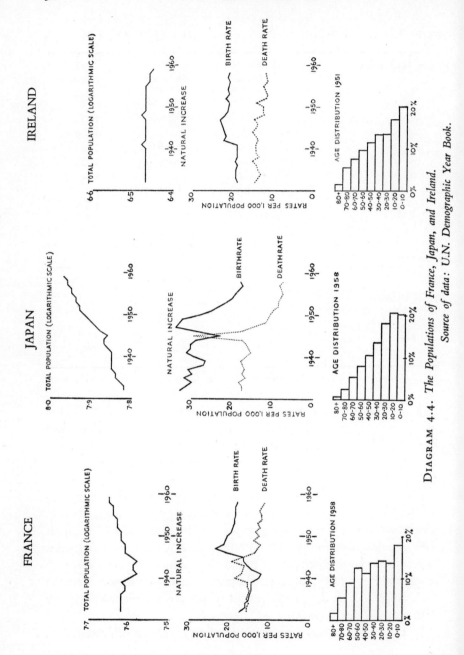

DIAGRAM 4.4. *The Populations of France, Japan, and Ireland.*
Source of data: U.N. Demographic Year Book.

for the majority of countries, the rate of natural increase is more important than the rate of migration. There are of course, some exceptions. Diagram 4.4. also gives information for Ireland, a country whose total population shows little change, since a reasonably steady rate of natural increase is offset by a high rate of emigration.

It will be useful to conclude this chapter with a short note on the sources of population statistics for England and Wales.

Population statistics may be collected in two very different ways. They may be obtained from the registration of events as they occur or they may be obtained from special inquiries of which the most important is the population census. Today the collection of both kinds of statistics is the responsibility of the Registrar-General. This office was created by an Act of Parliament in 1837 which provided for the civil registration of births and deaths.

National and regional data derived from registration statistics are published in the quarterly returns. More detailed analyses including those for all local authority areas are available in the Registrar-General's *Statistical Review* which is published annually.

The Census has always been used to obtain more information than the total number of persons in the population, though this is its primary purpose. At the first census, taken in 1801, questions were asked concerning the number of males and females in each family, the number of houses in which they lived and the occupations in which they were engaged.

Since 1801 the range of questions included in the census schedule has been extended and at times changed to meet the needs of government for various kinds of information. At the sixteenth census, taken in 1961, questions were asked concerning the birthplace, nationality, age, sex and marital status of persons; the composition of the households and the size and amenities of the dwellings in which they lived; the education and occupations of the working population, the industries in which they were engaged and their place of work. Information was also required, for the first time, concerning members of households who were absent on census night.

For the purpose of the census the country is divided into a number of Registration districts for each of which a Census Officer is appointed. These officers are usually, though not necessarily the local registrars of births, deaths and marriages. Each registration district is divided into a number of enumeration districts and an enumerator is appointed for each. For the 1961 Census about 70,000 enumerators were required.

The enumerators do more than deliver and collect the schedules. Responsibility for giving correct information rests with the householder, but the enumerator is expected to check that all questions are answered and to give help where necessary. The enumerators also make a list of all dwellings in their area, including those unoccupied at the time of the census and supply the data for the Preliminary Report. It is sometimes difficult to obtain a sufficient number of persons to act as enumerators: local government officers, civil servants, teachers, housewives and students have been employed for this work.

The completed schedules are sent by local Census Officers to headquarters where the data is coded and analysed. The modern census could not be undertaken without mechanical methods of processing data. Punched cards and Hollerith machines were first used for the census of 1911; an electronic computer is being used for the 1961 census.

In 1951 and again in 1961 sampling methods were used to reduce the time taken for the analysis; even so, the preparation of a complete set of census reports takes a considerable time. The results of the 1951 census were published in more than fifty volumes over a period of seven years.

Recommended Reading

The Census Explained. H. M. S. O. (pamphlet), 1951.
Why a Census? H. M. S. O. (pamphlet), 1961.
Report of the Royal Commission on the Population, Cmd. 7695. H. M. S. O., 1949.
Census of Population, England and Wales, 1951. General Report, H. M. S. O., 1958.
Matters of Life and Death, H. M. S. O. (pamphlet), 1956.
Wrong, D. H. Population. Random House, New York, 1956.
Determinants and Consequences of Population Trends, U. N., 1953.
Hogben, L. (Ed.) Political Arithmetic, George Allen & Unwin, 1938.
'The Baby Boom'. The Economist. July 29, 1961.

CHAPTER 5

THE ACCURACY OF STATISTICS

IN the social sciences it is rarely possible to obtain completely accurate statistics, but complete accuracy is seldom, if ever, necessary. It is sufficient to consider whether the available statistics are accurate enough for the purpose for which they are required. In practice this involves consideration of the most likely sources of error, and the nature and size of the errors that may occur.

Statistical enquiries are generally large scale enquiries and involve the collection of information from a large number of sources. It is inevitable that some errors will occur in the process. Such errors may be due to genuine mistakes made by persons taking part in the enquiry: they may be due to incomplete coverage or faulty record keeping; or they may be errors of approximation introduced in the process of summarizing the data. If sampling methods are used in the collection of statistics, their use introduces additional sampling errors.

Published statistics are frequently rounded off to the nearest hundred, thousand or million according to the nature of the data. All such estimates are liable to errors of rounding off, though of course they may be liable to other kinds of error as well. Errors of rounding off lie within a range of $\pm$ ·5 of the unit used. Since these errors are equally likely to be positive or negative, they may be described as unbiassed errors. Under some circumstances, as when a large number of rounded off estimates are added together, these errors tend to cancel each other out.

Clerical errors or genuine mistakes are also likely to be unbiassed errors. Their size cannot be easily determined, but since they are unbiassed they are likely to cancel each other out in a large scale enquiry.

Population census reports contain two sets of estimates of the enumerated population of all local authority areas. The preliminary report gives estimates which are made directly from the enumerators' records. The General Tables contain estimates made from an analysis of all the schedules. Any differences between these two sets of estimates can be regarded as clerical errors. For a sample of 90 local authority areas, the difference at the 1931 census was never more than ·66 per cent of the population and for the country as a whole it was very much less, being only 4,446 persons or about one tenth of one per cent of the total population. Errors in one area tended to cancel out errors in another.

On the other hand, errors due to incomplete coverage or faulty record keeping are likely to be biassed errors; i.e. all the estimates made from these enquiries are likely to be either too large or too small. Census estimates of national populations generally have a downward bias, since it is easier to omit persons who should have been included than it is to count the same person twice. There are, however, exceptions to this rule. The census of 1831 in Ireland was made by agents who were paid by results, with the consequence that the population estimates for some counties were certainly too high!

When a system of registration of births and deaths is introduced in any country it is rarely complete in the early years. Consequently improvements in the system of registration often appear to produce increases in both the birth-rate and the death-rate. This was certainly the case for Ceylon for which country statistics of births and deaths are available since 1871. During the decade 1871–1880 the birth-rate averaged 27·4 per 1,000 population and the death-rate averaged 22·8 per 1,000. The recorded rates increased more or less steadily until the decade 1911–1921 when they were 38·2 and 30·8 respectively. Since 1921, the birth-rate has been maintained at approximately this high level but the death-rate has fallen consistently. In this more recent period, the demographic history of Ceylon has been similar to that of other countries passing through the same stage of economic and cultural development. The apparent differences in the earlier period are more likely to be due to defective statistics than to an unusual pattern of development in Ceylon.

The collection of social and economic statistics generally involves asking many people to answer questions at some stage of the enquiry. The population census requries answers from all householders: the census of production depends on the replies of manufacturers: the census of distribution involves small shopkeepers as well as large retailers: many government departments derive part at least of their information from the returns of local authorities: statistics of imports and exports depend on information provided by importers and exporters. The accuracy of the final statistics therefore depends on the accuracy of many thousands of individuals. Genuine mistakes probably do not matter very much in large scale enquiries, since such mistakes, being unbiassed errors will largely cancel each other out. But biassed errors could easily occur if the informants had any incentive to give incorrect information, or if they found the questions too difficult to answer.

Here are some examples.

Generally it can be assumed that people will be willing and able to answer the fairly simple questions that are asked at the census of population. But from time to time questions have been asked which have presented difficulties.

At the 1951 census, there was a question concerning the number of rooms occupied by each household. This question has been asked at every census since 1891 and has usually been answered satisfactorily. In some areas, however, enumerators found an unexpected unwillingness to answer it. One explanation of this unwillingness is that people in these areas remembered war-time evacuation schemes and were afraid that the census information might be used for similar schemes in the future. Assurances were given that the information was only wanted for statistical purposes and the question was then answered satisfactorily.

There are however a number of topics on which it is very difficult to obtain reliable information. At the census of 1851 an attempt was made to obtain statistics concerning the number of "deaf and dumb" and "blind" persons. Questions on this subject were repeated with various alterations and additions at each census until 1911 in spite of the repeated protests of the Registrars-General that the information obtained in this way was of very little use. Householders did not or could not distinguish between the partially and totally blind; and when questions were included relating to imbeciles and idiots they were obviously unwilling to admit that any members of their households belonged to these categories.

The Ministry of Labour estimate that the results of their recent enquiry concerning household expenditure, though reasonably accurate in most respects, under-estimate personal expenditure on alcoholic drink by about one half and expenditure on tobacco by about one quarter. For these commodities independent estimates of expenditure can be made from Exchequer receipts. Similar difficulties were encountered in earlier enquiries of the same kind.

Today sampling methods are frequently used in the collection of economic and social statistics. In some cases such methods are used to obtain results quickly, e.g. the analysis of a one per cent sample for the 1951 Population Census was justified by the urgency of the need for census data. In other cases sampling methods are used to obtain information which it would be too difficult or too costly to obtain by other means. The social surveys used to forecast election results, to estimate the extent of poverty in a town and to assess the use made of various social services come into this category.

Sampling surveys are liable to the same kinds of error as other statistical enquiries; they suffer from errors of definition, incomplete coverage, wrong information and clerical mistakes. They are also liable to errors which arise from the sampling process itself.

Since samples include some members of the population but exclude others, the results from samples are unlikely to be exactly the same as those which would have been obtained from the whole population had such an enquiry been possible. The difference between the sample value and that for the whole population is known as the sampling error. This error cannot be known exactly, but sampling theory can be used to determine the limits within which it is likely to lie and so to assess the reliability of the estimates made from samples.

Sampling theory will not be discussed in this book, but there are many elementary statistical text-books which deal with this subject.

Ideally all published statistics should have a note attached giving an estimate of their reliability. This seldom happens in practice: but two cases in which estimates of errors are shown may be noted.

The United Nations publish annual estimates of total world populations: these estimates are based on information which is provided by individual governments and which varies considerably in reliability. Estimates of the possible error for the total population of the various regions into which the world is divided are given: these vary from 0.5 per cent for the countries of North America, Northern and Central Europe to 10 per cent for the countries of

East Asia. The total world population, which is given as 2,652 million for 1954, may be under-estimated by as much as 5 per cent.

The second example is provided by the National Income and Expenditure statistics for the United Kingdom: these are published annually by the Central Statistical Office.

The gross national income, or gross national product of a country may be defined as "the money value of the goods and services becoming available to the nation from economic activity". This is obviously an important aggregate, since it provides a measure of the economic resources available for current consumption, the maintenance of capital equipment and for further investment. It is also useful to know how this income is obtained and how it is spent. National Income statistics are therefore presented as a series of accounts designed to show the relationship between the various sectors of the economy: e.g. these accounts show the contribution of the various industries and overseas trade to the National Income: the division of this income between individuals, governments, public and private companies: the type of goods and services on which this income is spent. In such a series of estimates, it is natural that some should be more reliable than others. It is easier to estimate government than private income, easier to estimate large incomes which are subject to tax, than small incomes for which there are no such records: easier to obtain information about the financial position of public than private companies. In their recent publication, "National Income Statistics: Sources and Methods," the Central Statistical Office has graded its main totals according to their reliability. The best estimates, graded A, have errors which are probably less than ± 3 per cent: for those graded B, the errors are probably between ± 3 per cent and ± 10 per cent: the rest are graded C and for these the errors are probably more than ± 10 per cent. As many of the least reliable estimates form only a small part of the national income, the estimates of Gross National Product are graded A and so are more reliable than some of their components.

Many practical problems involve the comparison of statistics for different times: it is therefore necessary to consider the effect of errors in the original data on the accuracy of such comparisons. This effect will depend on both the size and the nature of the errors involved.

In some cases the comparisons between estimates will be more accurate, in others less accurate than the original estimates.

If all estimates are too large or too small by the same amount, the estimate of changes will be unaffected by errors in the original data. For example, the National Income and Expenditure blue book for 1956 gives the contribution of rent to the National Income as £716 millions in 1954 and £731 millions in 1955 an increase of £15 million. These estimates are graded B and are therefore probably subject to errors of at least ± £21 million. This suggests that the estimate of change is useless: but in this case the estimated increase in rent between 1954 and 1955 was taken into account in making the estimate for the later year. Consequently the estimate of change may be more reliable than the estimates of the total rent for either year.

Improvements in the statistical data which reduce the size of the errors may render comparisons difficult or even useless.

The United Nations statistical services have done much in recent years to improve the standard of census taking in less well developed countries. Consequently part of the recorded increase in world population in recent years is due to the better methods of counting which have been adopted. The Demographic Year Book for 1951 estimated the world population in 1950 as 2,400 millions: the 1955 Year Book raised this estimate to 2,455 millions.

Since 1891, the Census of Population has included a question designed to determine the extent to which Welsh is spoken in Wales. When this question was first asked in 1891, the schedules for use in Wales had a column headed "Language Spoken" and householders were asked to complete it in this way. "If only English, write English: if only Welsh, write Welsh: if English and Welsh write Both". This question should have been easy to answer, but there was plenty of evidence to show that the answers were biased. Many bilingual persons who should have answered both, actually answered Welsh, and many young infants were shown as speaking only Welsh! In analysing the results, the Census authorities excluded children under two years of age, but even so, the results over-estimated the proportion speaking only Welsh.

The same question was asked again at the Census of 1901 of all persons aged three years or more. Owing to the change in the minimum age, the estimates for the two years are not strictly comparable; but even allowing for this, some part of the recorded decline in the proportion of persons speaking only Welsh, from 30·1 per cent to 15·1 per cent must have been due to improvements in the statistics.

Another example of this kind of difficulty is shown in Table 5.1. This gives the number of graduate men teachers employed in maintained and assisted grammar schools in England and Wales in the years 1947–51 and the number of those graduates with degrees in mathematics and science. At first it may be difficult to reconcile the obvious increase in both the number and proportion of science teachers in this period with the remembered public concern for the acute shortage of such specialists. But this apparent increase in the proportion of science teachers may have been entirely due to better information. The proportion of teachers for whom the degree subject was not known declined in this period and the proportion of arts graduates also showed an increase.

TABLE 5.1

GRADUATE MEN TEACHERS IN FULL-TIME EMPLOYMENT IN MAINTAINED AND ASSISTED GRAMMAR SCHOOLS

Year	Number of Graduates	Number holding Science degrees ★	Percentage of graduates with science degrees	Percentage of graduates for whom subject is not known
1947	9,722	2,069	21	38
1948	10,911	3,140	29	24
1949	11,429	3,600	31	22
1950	11,897	4,151	25	16
1951	12,338	4,646	38	6·5

★ *includes mathematics*

Source of data: Ministry of Education Annual Reports.

If the errors in the original data are unbiassed and their maximum size is known, as is the case for rounding off errors, it is possible to calculate the maximum errors in the statistics derived from them.

There are two simple rules which may be used to determine the errors in sums, differences, products and quotients.

The maximum error in a sum or difference is equal to the sum of the maximum errors in the original quantities. The use of this rule

TABLE 5.2

ERRORS IN SUMS AND DIFFERENCES

Country	Source of Estimate	Estimate of Population (000's)	Error of Estimate (000's)
England and Wales	Abstract	42,700	± ·5
Scotland	Abstract	5,135	± ·5
Great Britain	By addition	47,835	± 1·0
United Kingdom	Abstract	49,185	± ·5
Northern Ireland	By Subtraction	1,350	± 1·5

N.B. This calculation only takes account of rounding off errors.

is illustrated in Table 5.2. which gives population estimates for countries of the United Kingdom derived from the Annual Abstract of Statistics. These data relate to 1946 and have been rounded off to the nearest thousand, and so are liable to errors of ± 500. Generally errors in differences will be more serious than errors in sums. The errors calculated in this way are, of course, maximum errors and the actual error is likely to be somewhat smaller. If all values in a table, including the total, are rounded off to some convenient unit, the total of any column and the sum of its components will not necessarily agree: since however the errors are unbiassed, they tend to cancel each other out and agreement is more common than disagreement.

When calculating products or quotients, it is convenient to express the errors as relative or percentage errors, since the maximum relative error in the product or quotient is the sum of the relative errors in the separate quantities.

For 1954, the total personal expenditure in the United Kingdom was estimated at £14,544 million: and the total population at the same date was 50,784,000: average expenditure per head of population was therefore £286·389. If these totals may be assumed correct to the nearest million and thousand respectively, the relative errors are only ·003 per cent and ·001 per cent respectively: in this case the error in the estimate of average expenditure per head is only ·004 per cent, i.e. about threepence. It would however, be more realistic to assume an error of ± 3 per cent in the expenditure estimate and ± ·5

TABLE 5.3

ERRORS IN ESTIMATES FROM DERIVED STATISTICS

Source of Income	Percentage of total income		Estimates of personal income £m.		Estimate of tax paid £m
	Before tax	After tax	Before tax	After tax	
Wages	45	47	4,626	4,084	541
Salaries	25	25	2,570	2,173	397
Pay of Armed Forces	2	3	206	261	—55
Rent, dividends and interest	28	25	2,878	2,173	706
Total £m.	10,279	8,690			

per cent for the population estimate. Under these circumstances the error in the estimate of average expenditure per head is $\pm$ 3·5 per cent, or roughly £10.

The errors in products are generally more serious than those in quotients, and it is usually dangerous to reverse the process and re-estimate a set of data from the derived statistics. The example of Table 5.3 should provide convincing evidence of these dangers.

The information given in the first part of the table has been derived from the National Income and Expenditure Estimates for the United Kingdom for 1950. From this information it is possible to estimate the money value of each of these components of personal income both before and after tax and so to derive estimates of the amount of tax paid in each case. But the estimates of tax paid are obviously unreliable, and in the case of the armed forces, patently absurd!

RECOMMENDED READING

Morgenstern, O. *On the Accuracy of Economic Observations*, Princeton University Press, 1950.

National Income Statistics: Sources and Methods, Central Statistical Office, Studies in Official Statistics 3, H. M. S. O. 1956.

Devons. E. 'The Language of Economic Statistics' (included in *Essays in Economics*) George Allen & Unwin Ltd., 1961.

EXERCISES I

I. I. Discuss the validity of the following arguments.

(i) In 1954, university degrees were awarded to 19,115 students and university diplomas to 7,186 students. It is clear from these figures that degree students were more successful than diploma students.

(ii) In 1951, 20 per cent of the urban population of Wales spoke Welsh: the corresponding proportion for the rural population was 44 per cent. Obviously the majority of the Welsh speaking population lived in rural areas.

(iii) "793 pupils of the Little-Town School of Motoring have passed their driving test. If you wish to be successful, enrol with us." — Advertisement.

I. 2. Draw a diagram or diagrams to illustrate the age-distributions of migrants to Corby and Worthing during the twelve months ended September 30, 1949.

| Age | Percentages | |
	Corby U.D.	Worthing M.B.
0–10	15·7	12·2
10–20	8·2	7·6
20–30	36·4	17·2
30–40	21·0	13·5
40–50	9·8	12·0
50–60	4·7	11·6
60 & over	4·2	25·9
Total	100·0	100·0

Source of data: Internal Migration. Newton M. P. and Jeffery J. R., G.R.O. Studies in Medical & Population Subjects No. 5, H.M.S.O. 1951.

I. 3. Comment on the information given below: it has been obtained from 1951 Census Reports. You may use diagrams and/or derived statistics to illustrate your answer.

	Eastbourne M.B.	Shrewsbury M.B.	Northampton C.B.	Darlington C.B.	Port Talbot M.B.
Total Population	57,821	44,926	104,432	84,886	44,024
Occupied Population	24,174	22,736	53,664	39,531	25,236
Men	14,483	15,395	33,301	27,669	21,732
Women	9,691	7,341	20,363	11,862	3,504
Numbers engaged in Agriculture, Forestry and Fishing	365	455	205	219	248
Mining & Manufacturing industry	3,270	5,775	28,706	19,472	13,535
Building & Contracting	2,512	1,439	3,148	2,334	4,808
Service Industries	18,027	15,067	21,605	17,506	6,645

I. 4. The following data have been taken from the annual reports of the Ministry of Education.

Graduate men teachers employed in full-time service in maintained and assisted schools. England & Wales 1948–56.

Year	All Schools	Primary	Secondary Modern	Secondary Technical	Secondary Grammar
1948	17,689	2,313	3,351	1,034	10,911
1949	18,362	2,295	3,572	979	11,429
1950	19,044	2,317	3,620	972	11,897
1951	19,932	2,349	3,901	1,056	12,338
1952	20,780	2,492	4,210	1,129	12,496
1953	21,863	2,697	4,607	1,254	12,776
1954	23,005	2,909	5,109	1,378	13,019
1955	24,067	3,077	5,485	1,430	13,328
1956	25,030	3,131	5,722	1,518	13,633

Illustrate them graphically using both ordinary and logarithmic scales. Comment on the relative advantages of each type of scale in this case.

I. 5. A non-statistical friend asks you the following questions. You have a copy of the Annual Abstract of Statistics for a recent year: what answers would you give? Consider carefully the definitions of all statistics you use.

    (i) How many school children are there in Great Britain?

    (ii) How many university students are studying economics?

    (iii) How much wheat is grown in this country?

    (iv) How many miles were flown by British aircraft last year?

I. 6. (a) "97 per cent of grammar school girls usually do homework each evening. The corresponding percentage for girls in secondary modern and technical schools is 39 per cent." Does this mean that 68 per cent of all secondary school girls usually do homework each evening?

(b) "In 1954, the case fatality rate from appendicitis with peritonitis was 3·3 per cent in teaching hospitals and 6·6 per cent in non-teaching hospitals." Does this mean that when a person suffering from these complaints is treated in a non-teaching hospital his chances of leaving the institution alive are only one half of what they would have been if he had chosen to be a patient at a teaching hospital?

PART II

AVERAGES AND INDEX NUMBERS

CHAPTER 6

AVERAGES AND WEIGHTED AVERAGES

A VERAGES are among the most useful of statistical measures. They summarize the information about a number of varying quantities in a single figure: e.g. it is usual in schools to find the average age of a class. Some children will be older than average, some younger, and there may be no one child who is exactly average age: nevertheless the average age provides useful information concerning the group as a whole.

Like all methods of summarizing data, the average leaves out a great deal. In particular, it provides no information concerning the variation about the average and this variation may be as important as the average itself. Two classes of school children may have the same average age, but present very different problems for the teacher if one class has only children aged 12 to 13 years and the other children 10 to 15 years, or even 8 to 18 years.

The measurement of variation and the various types of average that can be used will be considered in Part III. This chapter is only concerned with one type of average, the arithmetic mean and an important variant of it, the weighted arithmetic mean.

The arithmetic mean is defined as the sum of a set of quantities divided by the number of quantities, i.e. if there are n quantities, $X_1, X_2, X_3, \ldots X_n$ then their arithmetic mean is given by:

$$\frac{X_1 + X_2 + X_3 \ldots + X_n}{n}$$

This formula may be abbreviated by the use of a summation sign Σ (sigma) and there are several convenient and generally accepted symbols for the arithmetic mean.

$$\text{A.M.} = \overline{X} = m = \frac{\Sigma X}{n}$$

In calculating this average, each value of X is counted once and once only. In many problems however, some values of X are more important than others, and a weighted average is used to take account of this fact. Suppose that corresponding to each value $X_1, X_2, X_3 \ldots$ X_n there is a quantity or weight, $w_1, w_2, w_3 \ldots w_n$ which in some way measures the importance of the corresponding value of X, then a weighted arithmetic mean can be obtained using the formula:

$$\text{Wtd. A.M.} = \frac{w_1X_1 + w_2X_2 + w_3X_3 + \ldots + w_nX_n}{w_1 + w_2 + w_3 + \ldots + w_n} = \frac{\Sigma wX}{\Sigma w}$$

The following simple examples should make the use of this formula clear.

Suppose a greengrocer is selling three kinds of nuts at 3s. 4s. and 5s. per pound respectively. Then an average price for these three sorts of nuts could be obtained by adding the three prices together and dividing by three. This average would be 4s. but the greengrocer might object that this average was of no interest to him, since he sold four times as many 3s. nuts as either 4s. or 5s. nuts. In this case the greengrocer would prefer a weighted average for which the weights would be proportional to the quantities sold.

$$\text{i.e. Wtd. A. M.} = \frac{4 \times 3 + 1 \times 4 + 1 \times 5}{4 + 1 + 1} \text{ s.}$$
$$= \text{3s. 6d}$$

Or suppose a factory employs both skilled and unskilled women workers: the former earn £7 per week, and the latter £5 per week. The arithmetic mean of these two amounts is £6, but it may bear little relation to the wage bill for this particular factory. In this case a weighted average, with weights proportional to the numbers employed would be more meaningful. If the factory employed three times as many unskilled as skilled workers, the average earnings of the workers would be given by:

$$\text{Wtd. A.M.} = \frac{£1 \times 7 + 3 \times 5}{1 + 3} = £5.10.0d$$

It is important to consider the accuracy of this type of calculation. If the errors in the weights and quantities are known, the maximum errors in the average can be found using the methods of Chapter 5, e.g. if the weights can be regarded as exact and the quantities are rounded off to the nearest unit, the maximum error in the average will be ± ·5 units. It is very likely that the actual error will be much smaller than this, particularly if the number of quantities to be averaged is large: rounding off errors are unbiassed errors, some will be positive and others negative and they will tend to cancel each other out.

Most practical problems involve the use of approximate weights: their use reduces the arithmetic involved, and providing the approximation is not too rough, will give sufficiently accurate results for most purposes. The use of approximate weights is illustrated in Table 6.1.

TABLE 6.1
THE USE OF APPROXIMATE WEIGHTS

Industry	Average weekly earnings (s.)	Numbers employed, used as weights			
		(1)	(2)	(3)	(4)
A	189·25	408,719	4,087	409	41
B	195·33	20,613	206	21	2
C	210·50	185,688	1,857	186	19
Average weekly earnings for all industries (s.)		195·870	195·870	195·874	195·958

The saving in arithmetic achieved by using approximate weights (2) instead of the original figures, is very considerable, but does not affect the accuracy of the average if calculated to three decimal places. The approximation of weights (3) would be reasonable for most purposes and even the drastic approximation of weights (4) leaves the whole numbers unchanged.

The fact that approximate weights will generally give satisfactory results does not mean that any change in the weighting system is unimportant. Changes in the weights, particularly if they are related to changes in the variable involved, can have a very marked effect on the value of the averages. The following imaginary and somewhat exaggerated example (Table 6.2.) illustrates this point. All prices have risen but the average price is unchanged because of the accompanying change in the weights.

Many statistics are really averages or weighted averages, although

TABLE 6.2

EXAMPLE TO ILLUSTRATE IMPORTANCE
OF WEIGHTING SYSTEM

Commodity	Average 1.			Average 2.		
	Prices (s)	Wts.	Price x Weight	Prices (s)	Wts.	Price x Weight
A	2	8	16·0	2·5	14	35·0
B	3	6	18·0	3·5	3	10·5
C	4	4	16·0	4·5	1	4·5
Totals		18	50·0		18	50·0
Weighted Average			2·8s.			2·8s.

they are not always regarded as such. It is useful to recognize that many national statistics are the average of a series of values for individual regions or districts within the country, e.g. during the twenty years 1931–1951, the population of England and Wales increased by 9 per cent, but this is an average of the increases and decreases for a large number of areas. At one extreme were areas such as Huyton with Roby and Corby which increased by more than 900 per cent: at the other extreme were those London boroughs which lost as much as 50 per cent of their 1931 populations.

The national unemployment percentage is a useful guide to the general economic situation, but it must always be remembered that some areas are more prosperous and others less prosperous than this average suggests. In December 1957, unemployment for the United Kingdom was only 1·6 per cent but for Northern Ireland, Wales and Scotland the percentages were 7·6, 3·0 and 2·9 respectively, whereas the Midlands, north Midlands, and the East and West Ridings of Yorkshire had only one per cent unemployment. During the economic depression of the thirties, unemployment rates were much higher, but they were also subject to wide regional differences. For 1932, the average for Great Britain was 22·2 per cent, but the rate for Wales was 36·5 per cent and that for London only 13·5 per cent. For smaller areas the range of variation was naturally much greater. Leicester, a relatively prosperous town, had a rate of 8 per cent, but some districts in South Wales had rates as high as 60 per cent.

Whenever averages are being compared, it is advisable to look for an explanation of the differences in changes of the weighting system as well as in changes of the quantities themselves.

In a sample survey of student opinion made at Leicester in 1954, students were asked what salaries they hoped or expected to get in their first job. Many did not know what to expect, but among those who replied, the average for science students was £547 per annum and that for arts students £445. It is certainly true that the scientists expected better starting salaries than the arts students, but the difference between them was not as great as the above figures suggest. Both these averages are weighted averages for men and women students: the men expected better salaries than the women in both faculties, but the science students included a higher proportion of men than the arts students. As the number of women students answering this question was relatively small, it is desirable to restrict the comparison to the expected salaries of men students. These were £552 and £490 for the science and arts faculties respectively.

Since the value of weighted averages is influenced by changes in the weights as well as by changes in the quantities, the comparison of averages with different sets of weights can often be used to assess the relative importance of the factors involved in any problem.

An example is given in Table 6.3. This gives information concerning employment and average earnings in the main industry groups in England, Wales and Scotland. The average annual earnings for all industries for these three countries were £319, £314 and £300 respectively. The differences in these averages could be due to differences in the amounts to be earned in the same industry in each of these countries, or they could be due to differences in the proportions of work people employed in the better paid industries, or they could be due to a combination of both these factors. To determine which of these explanations is most satisfactory in this case, it is useful to obtain a series of weighted averages to show the earnings of each group of workers when paid at different regional rates. In Table 6.3. all possible combinations of average earnings and employment have been used and nine averages have been calculated, e.g. if English workers received the same average earnings as Welsh workers in those same industries, their average earnings would be found as follows:

Average earnings for English workers at Welsh "rates" ...

$$= \pounds \, \frac{43 \times 222 + 37 \times 366 + ... + 90 \times 211}{1000} = \pounds 308$$

From the results it is clear that England had the advantage of higher regional earnings rates than either Wales or Scotland but that Wales had a more advantageous industrial structure than either of the other two countries.

TABLE 6.3

EMPLOYMENT AND EARNINGS IN GREAT BRITAIN, 1948

Industry	Numbers employed per 1,000			Average earnings £ per annum		
	Eng.	Wales	Scotl.	Eng.	Wales	Scotl.
Agriculture	43	49	63	292	222	255
Mining	37	160	49	390	366	392
Manufacturing	404	277	372	315	321	289
Building	64	68	72	318	305	320
Gas, Electricity and Water	16	15	12	347	320	323
Transport and Communication	89	102	94	372	363	356
Distribution	100	92	113	282	257	256
Finance	22	12	15	462	421	421
Public Administration	72	79	60	353	310	330
Professional Services	63	66	71	343	344	348
Miscellaneous Services	90	80	79	225	211	212
All industries	1000	1000	1000	319	314	300
Average earnings	at English	"rates"		319	329	319
,, ,,	,, Welsh	,,		308	314	306
,, ,,	,, Scottish	,,		299	313	300

Source of data: P. Deane: Regional variations in U.K. incomes from Employment J.R.S.S. 1953.

The study of mortality provides many examples of the use of weighted averages.

Crude death rates are obtained by relating the number of deaths to the total population in which they occur. They are usually expressed as the number of deaths per 1,000 living at the middle of the period for which they are calculated, and this is generally one year. Since the risk of dying varies with age, the crude death-rate is affected by the age-composition of a population as well as by its healthiness. Consequently such rates are unsuitable for the comparison of populations which differ greatly in this respect. For instance, the crude death-rates for England and Wales for the years 1901 and 1951 were 16·9 and 12·5 respectively, but the improvement in mortality rates in these fifty years was much greater than these crude death-rates suggest. The population of 1951 contained a much higher proportion of old persons than that of 1901, and this factor tended to raise the crude death-rate.

For purposes of comparison, the effect of differences in the age-composition of two populations can be eliminated by the calculation of standardized death-rates. In this case, the death-rate for a population with the same age composition as the population of 1901 and the mortality rates for specific age groups of 1951 can be found. The calculation is shown in Table 6.4. and the standardized death-rate for

TABLE 6.4

MORTALITY RATES FOR ENGLAND AND WALES

Ages	Deathrate per 1000 population		Total Population (000's)		Product of columns (3) and (4)
	1901	1951	1901	1951	
(1)	(2)	(3)	(4)	(5)	(6)
0– 4	54·2	6·54	3,716	3,722	24302·64
5– 9	4·06	0·56	3,487	3,187	1952·72
10–14	2·34	0·47	3,342	2,829	1570·74
15–19	3·34	0·76	3,247	2,715	2467·72
20–24	4·24	1·13	3,121	2,879	3526·73
25–34	5·75	1·46	5,256	6,341	7673·76
35–44	9·62	2·62	3,995	6,708	10466·90
45–54	15·9	6·89	2,902	6,014	19994·78
55–64	29·8	18·0	1,942	4,592	34956·00
65–74	61·5	46·3	1.075	3,250	49772·50
75–84	129·8	117·9	393	1,372	46334·70
85 and over	258·0	280·9	49	191	13764·10
All ages	16·9	12·5	32,525	43,800	216783·29

Source of data: Registrar-General's Statistical Review, 1951.
Annual Abstract of Statistics.

Standardized deathrate for 1951 = 216783·29 ÷ 32,525
= 6·7 per 1,000.

1951 is 6·7 deaths per 1,000 population. This standardized rate may be compared with the crude or all-ages death-rate for 1901 of 16·9 per 1,000. Using this method of comparison, average mortality rates had fallen by about 60 per cent in these fifty years, although the crude rate had only fallen by about one quarter.

Standardized rates of this kind, using the 1901 population as a standard population were used for many years to measure annual changes in mortality for the country as a whole. Since the 1901 population was a very young population, this method of standardization gives considerable weight to improvements in mortality rates for children and infants. Consequently as the proportion of old persons in the population has increased, this method of standardization has become progressively less satisfactory. Alternative methods which give greater weight to changes in mortality rates at the older ages have therefore been adopted. During the years 1942–58 the Comparative Mortality Index was used and in 1958 this index was replaced by a Standardized Mortality Ratio.

The Comparative Mortality Index is essentially the ratio of two standardized rates, one for the current year, or the year for which the index is calculated and one for the base year in this case 1938. The standard population used for the calculation of these rates is an average of the populations for 1938 and the current year.* The values of this index for 1901 and 1951 (1938 = 1·000) were 1·811 and ·901 respectively. This index shows a smaller estimate of the improvement in mortality rates during the first half of the century than is obtained by comparing the standardized rates, 16·9 and 6·7. This is only to be expected, since as can be seen from Table 6.4., the most important improvements in mortality rates have occurred at the younger ages. These improvements are weighted less heavily in the Comparative Mortality Index, than in the standardized death-rate.

Standardized Mortality Ratios are obtained by expressing the actual number of deaths registered in any year as a percentage of the number that would have been expected if the death-rates at individual

---

* Suppose $m_1, m_2 \ldots$ and $M_1, M_2 \ldots$ are the mortality rates for individual age-groups in the years 1938 and X respectively: and that the proportions of the total population in these same age-groups are $r_1 r_2 \ldots$ and $R_1 R_2 \ldots$ for these same years,

$$\text{then C:M.I. for Year } X = \frac{\Sigma M(r+R)}{\Sigma m(r+R)}$$

ages had remained unchanged. The data of Table 6.4. can be used to calculate the S.M.R. for 1951 using 1901 as base year.

$$\text{Actual number of deaths in 1951} = 12 \cdot 5 \times 43{,}800$$
$$= 547{,}500$$

$$\frac{\text{Expected number of deaths in 1951}}{\text{at 1901 rates}} = \frac{\text{Sum of products of}}{\text{columns (2) and (5)}}$$
$$= 1{,}003{,}261$$

$$\text{S.M.R. 1951. (1901)} = 100) = \frac{547{,}500}{1{,}003{,}261} \times 100$$
$$= 55$$

This S.M.R. can be regarded as the ratio of the all ages death-rate for 1951 and the death-rate for 1901 standardized by the 1951 population. It shows a smaller improvement in the years 1901–1951 than the C.M.I. since the 1951 population is 'older' than the average of the 1951 and 1901 populations.

The S.M.R.'s. which are now published annually in the Registrar-General's Statistical Review use the average of the years 1950–52 as base year. Generally women live longer than men and death-rates for females are lower than those for males of the same age: consequently S.M.R.'s are calculated for males and females as well as persons, and in calculating ratios for persons, account has to be taken of the difference in male and female mortality.

Comparisons for local populations at the same date are made rather differently. Three statistics are available for each local authority area: the crude death rate, a comparability factor and the ratio of the local adjusted death rate to the national death rate. Table 6.5. gives this information for Leicester, Torquay and Corby. Of these towns, Torquay has the highest and Corby the lowest crude death rate. The comparability factor measures the extent to which the age-structure of the local population affects the crude death rate for the area. Where the comparability factor is less than one, as at Torquay, the population is older than the average for England and Wales: where it is greater than one, as at Corby, the population is younger than the national population. Leicester's population is almost average in this respect.

TABLE 6.5
MORTALITY RATES FOR THREE TOWNS

Town	Crude death rate (per 1,000 pop.)	Comparability Factor	Ratio of local adjusted death rate to national rate
Leicester C.B.	12·4	1·01	1·00
Torquay M.B.	17·6	0·69	0·97
Corby U.D.	6·4	1·77	0·91

Source: Registrar-General's Statistical Review, 1951.

The adjusted local death rate is obtained by multiplying the crude death rate by the comparability factor: this is equivalent to a standardized rate. For these towns, the adjusted death-rates are Leicester 12·5, Torquay 12·1 and Corby 11·3. These rates may be compared directly, or expressed as ratios to the national rate as in the third column of Table 6.5. Both comparisons show that the difference in the mortality experience of these three towns is not nearly as great as their crude death rates suggest.

Comparisons of mortality rates for various local populations and occupational groups have played an important part in the administration of public health. The rates for healthy populations can be used as a standard by which to judge conditions among less healthy populations. An interesting example of this use of mortality rates in the cause of social reform can be found in the work of Florence Nightingale.

When Miss Nightingale returned to England after the Crimean War in 1856, she was particularly concerned with the state of army barracks, which were insanitary and unhealthy, but she found it difficult to convince either the government or the generals that something could and should be done to remedy this. She therefore decided to obtain some statistics to support her case. She compared the death rates among soldiers in barracks with civilians living in the same neighbourhood, and was able to show that the army death rate was higher and generally much higher than the civilian rate. For example the civilian death rate in St. Pancras was 2·2 per 100, and that for the Life Guards stationed in the same borough was 10·4 per 100. As Miss Nightingale pointed out, the comparison was much more serious than these figures suggested, since the civilian population included the very young and the very old, whereas the soldiers were all young adults chosen for their physical fitness. These statistics were printed privately: they were found convincing and eventually the necessary reforms were undertaken.

RECOMMENDED READING

Wodeham-Smith, C. *Florence Nightingale*, Constable, 1950. Revised and slightly abridged version published in Penguin Books. 1955. Newsholme, A. *Vital Statistics*, George Allen & Unwin, 1923. Benjamin. B. *Elements of Vital Statistics*, George Allen and Unwin, 1959.

CHAPTER 7

THE RETAIL PRICE INDEX

RETAIL price indices of the cost of living type are calculated today by many governments. These indices are designed to measure changes in the prices of a fixed "basket" of consumer goods and services, and the contents of the basket are chosen so as to reflect the pattern of expenditure of a very large group of consumers. The methods used in the calculation of such an index can easily be understood by considering a simple imaginary example.

Suppose there is a schoolboy who spends all his pocket money on three commodities, bus fares to school, sweets and a weekly visit to the cinema. The value of this boy's pocket money will depend upon the prices of these commodities and the relative amounts that he spends on each. His pocket money price index can therefore be obtained by comparing the cost of the same number of bus journeys, the same quantity of sweets and identical seats in the cinema at different dates. It is simply the ratio of these aggregate costs, expressed as a percentage. This method of calculation is illustrated in Table 7.1.

The same result can be obtained by calculating the weighted average of a set of price relatives or price indices, one for each com-

TABLE 7.1

CALCULATION OF A PRICE INDEX — METHOD I

Commodity	Quantity bought	Prices		Cost of Commodities	
		Year I	Year II	Year I	Year II
		s. d	s. d	s. d	s. d
Bus journeys	10 journeys	4	5 per jrny.	3. 4	4. 2
Sweets	$\frac{1}{2}$ lb	1. 6	2. 0 per lb	9	1. 0
Cinema	1 seat in stalls	2. 3	2. 0 per seat	2. 3	2. 0
			Total cost	6. 4	7. 2

$$\text{Price Index Year II (Year I = 100)} = \frac{86}{76} \times 100$$

$$= 113\tfrac{3}{19}$$

or 113 to nearest unit

TABLE 7.2
CALCULATION OF A PRICE INDEX — METHOD 2

Commodity	Price Index Year II (Yr. I = 100)	Weights (cost in Year I)	Price Index × Weight
Bus journeys	125	40	5,000
Sweets	$133\frac{1}{3}$	9	1,200
Cinema	$88\frac{8}{9}$	27	2,400
Totals		76	8,600

$$\text{Price Index Year II (Year I} = 100) = \frac{8600}{76}$$

$$= 113 \text{ to nearest unit}$$

modity. The weights are determined from the expenditure at the first or base, date. This alternative method of calculation is shown in Table 7.2.

Either calculation can be extended to cover any number of years and to include many more commodities. Although the first method may appear to be simpler than the second, the latter is generally found more convenient in practice, and it is the method used by the Ministry of Labour for the calculation of the Index of Retail Prices.

The present index was begun in January 1956. It measures monthly changes in the prices of nearly 350 goods and services which are bought by the majority of households in this country. The choice of items and the weighting system used to combine their prices were determined from the results of a household budget enquiry made in 1953–54. The 350 items are grouped into ten main groups, Food, Alcoholic Drink, Tobacco, Housing, Fuel and Light, Durable Household Goods, Clothing and Footwear, Transport and Vehicles, Miscellaneous Goods and Services. Monthly indices are available for each of these groups in addition to the all items index, and the indices for some important sub-groups are available at quarterly intervals. This information is published in the *Ministry of Labour Gazette* and the *Monthly Digest of Statistics*.

Several methods are used for the collection of prices for this index. The majority of food prices are obtained by visits of the Ministry of Labour officials to shops in 200 local office areas. These 200 offices are chosen in such a way that all sizes and types of town are represented including the small towns in which the households of agricultural workers do their shopping. Some of these areas are at the centre of large industrial towns, others are in the suburbs. Information is obtained from five retailers in each area except in the case of some of the smaller towns in which fewer shops are used. If possible, these five retailers include a branch of the local co-operative society and a branch of a chain store.

The prices of furniture, floor coverings, domestic appliances such as electric irons, suit-cases, sports goods, clocks and gramophone records are also obtained by visits to shops. For these goods, however, the inquiry is limited to 23 large towns.

The prices of most other commodities are obtained by post, though changes in the rents of privately owned dwellings which are let unfurnished are obtained by interviewing a representative sample of tenants.

Prices of proprietory brands of tinned and packaged goods used to be obtained from the manufacturers; but now that the practice of selling at cut prices has grown considerably they are also obtained from a sample of shops. For clothes, footwear, soft-furnishings and china-ware, prices are obtained from several hundred retailers. Regional officers of the Ministry of Fuel and Power provide information concerning the prices of gas, coke and electricity in the same 200 towns for which food prices are collected. Prices of beer and other alcoholic drinks are obtained from brewery companies, those of cigarettes from the manufacturers. Information concerning the rents of council houses is obtained from the local authorities.

Regular inquiries are not necessary to determine changes in the cost of such things as car and motor-cycle licenses and inland postage.

The prices obtained by the Ministry of Labour are intended to be the prices at which goods are actually sold in the shops. These prices do not include extra charges for credit or hire-purchase: nor is any allowance made for co-operative society dividends which are only paid to members. Sale prices are only used, if all goods of the same kind are sold at these prices. Periodic checks are made to determine whether shops are selling at manufacturers' prices or not.

Since the index is designed to measure changes in the cost of a fixed "basket of goods", it is desirable that prices should be obtained for exactly the same articles each month. This is not always possible: some commodities are only available at certain times of the year and many of the goods which are sold in the shops vary in quantity or quality or are subject to changes in fashion. In some cases it is fairly easy to adjust the price index to take account of these changes; in others it is more difficult.

In times of rising prices, manufacturers may prefer to reduce the quantity of biscuits in the packet, or milk in the tin, rather than increase the price per packet or tin. Since however the customer now receives less for her money, such a change should be reflected as a price increase in the index. An interesting example of this type of adjustment occurred in 1950 when utility mattresses were reduced in thickness from 4 inches to 3½ inches and the price of mattresses used to calculate the index was increased to compensate for this change.

The change from new to old potatoes is both a seasonal and a quality change. New potatoes have a higher nutritional value and are less wasteful in use, than old potatoes. It may be assumed that up to mid-July of each year, 5½ lb of new potatoes are equivalent to 7 lb of old potatoes, but the relative advantage of new potatoes decreases with time. By mid-August 6 lb of new potatoes are needed to provide the equivalent of 7 lb of old potatoes and by mid-September this quantity must be increased to 6½ lb. By the next month, new potatoes may be regarded as old potatoes. The price index for potatoes is therefore obtained by comparing the prices of these quantities of new or old potatoes with the price of 7 lb of potatoes at January 1956 when the index was begun. During those months in which both old and new potatoes are on sale, the index is obtained by combining the indices for both types of potato according to the quantities in which they are being sold.

Many other examples of the need to allow for quality changes could be given. The price series for beer takes account of changes in the alcoholic content of this drink: the price series for sausages is adjusted to allow for changes in their meat content. It has not been possible to make adjustments for the varying quality and quantity of a portion of fish and chips: consequently this commodity has been excluded from the index. In this case the weights for fresh fish and potatoes have been increased to compensate for this omission.

Similar problems of changes in the quantity and quality of the goods sold occur in connection with clothing prices. Fashions change continuously and it is not always possible to obtain a series of prices for exactly the same garment each month. Retailers are asked to help in this case by quoting the price for the nearest substitute and to explain any differences between it and the original article. This problem is more serious in the case of furniture and household appliances. The latter goods, in particular, are subject to technical improvements as well as changes in fashion. For these goods prices are obtained by personal visits to shops in a few large towns, so that these difficulties may be studied carefully.

This description of the methods used to obtain the prices from which the index is calculated is by no means complete. Even so it is clear that each monthly index is built up from a large number of prices from a variety of sources. The calculation is therefore made in a number of stages.

The prices obtained for any particular month are compared with the prices of the same commodities at the base date, in this case, 17th January 1956, and a price relative or price index is obtained for each item, and for each source of supply. These price relatives are then averaged to give a price index for each item for the United Kingdom as a whole.

The items are grouped with related goods and services, first into sections and then into major groups. The number of items in a section, or sections in a group, varies considerably. The food group contains thirty-one sections, including those of flour, beef, butter, potatoes and icecream: the tobacco group contains only two sections, those for cigarettes and pipe tobacco respectively. Three types of loaf are priced for the bread section, and two kinds of flour for the flour section, but prices are obtained for fourteen cuts of home and imported beef. The indices for the sections are averages of the indices for the items included in them: and the group indices are weighted averages of the section indices. The all items index is a weighted average of the indices for the groups: this final calculation is illustrated in Table 7.3.

TABLE 7.3

U.K. INDEX OF RETAIL PRICES, DECEMBER 1957

(January 17, 1956 = 100)

	Group	Index (1)	Weight (2)	Product Columns (1) and (2)
I.	Food	106·0	350	37100·0
II.	Alcoholic Drink	105·7	71	7504·7
III.	Tobacco	107·8	80	8624·0
IV.	Housing	116·9	87	10170·3
V.	Fuel and Light	115·6	55	6358·0
VI.	Durable Household Goods	101·3	66	6685·8
VII.	Clothing & Footwear	103·0	106	10918·0
VIII.	Transport and Vehicles	112·7	68	7663·6
IX.	Miscellaneous Goods	111·6	59	6584·4
X.	Services	114·2	58	6623·6
	All items		1000	108232·4

$$\text{Index for all items} = \frac{108232\cdot4}{1000} = 108\cdot23$$

= 108 to nearest whole number

Index for all items except Groups II and III

$$= \frac{92103\cdot7}{849} = 108\cdot48$$

= 108 to nearest whole number.

Source of data: Ministry of Labour Gazette, January 1958.

It is possible to calculate other indices from this data, e.g. the non-smoker and non-drinker might be interested in an index which omitted these groups, though for the data given in Table 7.3., this omission has no effect on the index when calculated to the nearest whole number.

The present index of retail prices replaced an interim index which was begun in June 1947 and revised in January 1952: and this interim index replaced the Cost of Living Index which had been published for about thirty years.

The Cost of Living Index was first calculated during the 1914–18 war. It was designed to measure changes in the cost of maintaining the 1914 standard of living of the working classes and it was assumed that a fixed standard of living could be achieved by the purchase of the same set of commodities over a period of time. No information was available concerning working class expenditure in 1914, but the Board of Trade had made an inquiry into the cost of living in towns in 1904. Although wages and prices had both risen in the ten years 1904 to 1914, it was generally agreed that the working class standard of living had not changed and that consequently the 1904 inquiry provided satisfactory data for the choice of commodities and the weighting system for the cost of living index.

The priced commodities were divided into five main groups: food, rent and rates, clothing, fuel and light and other items: the weights allocated to these groups were 60, 16, 12, 8 and 4 respectively.

At the time when the index was first calculated, war-time inflation was causing prices to rise faster than wages and there was a considerable danger of strikes which would have interfered with the war effort. The index was therefore used to adjust wage-rates and to prevent the standard of living of the working classes falling below the 1914 level. At the end of the war, a number of trade unions negotiated sliding scale agreements with employers' associations, so that minimum wage rates in these industries varied automatically with the price index. The wage rates of many other workers were affected indirectly by changes in the Cost of Living Index, since it was widely quoted in wage negotiations. An index of such practical importance naturally attracted much publicity and criticism, but it was not until 1936 that the Government decided that it should be revised.

By the mid-nineteen-thirties the index was certainly out of date. The weighting system no longer represented the working class pattern of expenditure: the weight for food was over-estimated, that for other items much too low. Many important commodities were not included in the index, though some which were included had become unimportant. The only vegetable included in the index was potatoes: fresh fruits were omitted altogether: the index included candles but not electricity.

In order to revise the weighting system and the list of commodities included in the index, the Ministry of Labour undertook a new enquiry into working class expenditure. During the year beginning September 1937, budgets were collected from more than 12,000 working class households, for four weeks, at quarterly intervals. The results of this enquiry were available at the end of 1940 but it was considered unwise to change the cost of living index during the war: consequently the old index was continued for a number of years.

The results of the 1937–38 enquiry provided evidence of the changes that had taken place in working class expenditure since 1914. There was first of all an important change in the distribution of expenditure between the main groups. This is shown in Table 7.4.

TABLE 7.4

COMPARISON OF WEIGHTS USED IN COMPILING THE COST OF LIVING INDEX WITH THOSE SHOWN BY 1937–38 HOUSEHOLD BUDGET ENQUIRY

Items	Weights from Cost-of-Living Index — 1914 Expenditure	Weights based on 1937–38 budgets
Food	60	40·1
Rent and Rates	16	12·7*
Clothing	12	9·5
Fuel and Light	8	7·6**
Other items (1)	4	8·1
(2)	—	22·0
All items	100	100·0

Source: Cmd. 7077.

* Based on total expenditure on housing, including repayments to Building Societies.
** Including electricity, coke and firewood not included in index.

Although the biggest changes occurred in the food and other items groups, the proportion of total expenditure allocated to rent and rates, clothing and fuel and light, had also declined. Several factors had helped to bring about these changes. Average household expenditure had increased more than average prices. Working class households were better off in 1937–38 than they had been in 1914: consequently a smaller proportion of their expenditure was needed for necessities and a larger proportion was available for other things, many of which are here included in the other items groups.

Relative changes in the prices of the various commodities also affected the distribution of expenditure between the main groups. Food prices had not risen as much as other prices, consequently relatively less money was needed to buy the same amount of food. Also technical changes which had occurred in the intervening years made it possible for working class households to buy many goods and services in 1937 which had not been available in 1914: these included electricity, radio and various types of textiles.

It should also be noted that the weighting system of the Cost of Living Index could not have been an accurate reflection of working class expenditure in 1914. The weight of other items was certainly under-estimated since beer was omitted from the index. The budgets of the 1937-38 enquiry also underestimate expenditure on alcoholic drink to some extent. Experience shows that this type of expenditure is never fully disclosed in a household budget enquiry.

At the end of the second world war, the Government again considered the revision of the index. A Cost of Living Advisory Committee was appointed in 1946 and presented its report the next year. The committee recommended that the Cost of Living Index should be discontinued and its place taken by an Interim Index of Retail Prices. This change was made in June, 1947.

When it was first introduced, the interim index covered about 270 items divided into eight main groups. The weighting system was obtained by estimating the cost of working class consumption in 1937-38 at June 1947 prices, and the index measured average changes in prices from the same month. The index was revised in January 1952: several new commodities were included and the number of main groups increased to nine.

The new index differed in many important respects from the old index. The purpose of the index was re-defined. It was described as an index "which measures monthly changes in the prices of those goods and services in which the Household Budget Enquiry of 1937-38 had shown working class families to be interested." When the decision was taken to revise the index in 1936, the intention was simply to bring the Cost of Living Index up-to-date by changing the weighting system and including a wider range of commodities. By 1946 it was clear that more radical changes were required.

There are many costs of living which are not prices, e.g. income tax and national insurance contributions. Also many persons receive services for which they do not pay directly, e.g. the health and education services. Changes in the rates of taxes and variations in the social services can affect the cost of living, but since no prices are involved such changes cannot be included in a retail price index, however comprehensive. These considerations were more important in 1947 than in 1914 or in 1938. Also as the discussion of changes in working class expenditure has shown, the pattern of consumption is constantly changing. During this period as a whole, the changes were indicative of rising standards of living: but even if standards had not risen, the pattern of consumption could not have remained unchanged. It would have been affected by changes in overseas trade, technical changes in industry, changes in fashion and changes in the age composition of the population.

Under these circumstances it is not possible to accept a retail price index as a measure of changes in the cost of maintaining an unchanged standard of living. The change in the name of the index is significant of developments that had taken place in the theory of index numbers. Nevertheless the retail price index measures a very important aspect of changes in the cost of living, and like its predecessor, the cost of living index, it is frequently used in wage negotiations. Inevitably this has meant that it has also been the subject of much publicity and much criticism.

Many of these criticisms were due to the economic circumstances of the years 1947–1955, rather than to any defects in the index itself. A price index is an average: like all averages it is more meaningful and consequently more useful when the quantities being averaged do not vary too much amongst themselves. During this period, average prices rose rapidly, but some prices rose more rapidly than others, while at times some prices even declined. The great variation in price changes during this period is illustrated in Diagram 7.1. Owing to changes in the construction of the index, the diagram is only drawn for the years 1952–55, but it is typical of the longer period 1947–55.

Housewives are generally more conscious of food prices than other prices, since food must be bought every week or even every

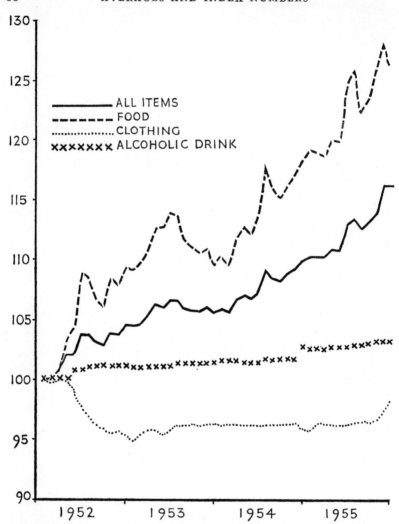

DIAGRAM 7.1. *Retail Prices in the United Kingdom 1952–5 (1952 = 100).*
Source of data: Ministry of Labour Gazette.

day. During these years, food prices were among those which rose
most. This fact may have accounted for the belief expressed by many
people that the retail price index underestimated the rise in prices.
Also the weighting system which is representative of working

class expenditure as a whole may not be representative for all groups within the working class. Families with several young children or those consisting of old-age pensioners tend to spend a higher proportion of their income on food, than do families of adults. It was therefore only natural that important groups within the working class should feel that the index did not measure price changes as experienced by their own group.

The Interim Index of Retail Prices was revised for the second time at the beginning of 1956, when information from the 1953–54 Household Budget Enquiry became available.

For this enquiry a sample of households were asked to keep records for three consecutive weeks: at the same time all adult members of the household were required to keep records of their personal expenditure and a number of questions were asked concerning insurance and other payments which only occur at frequent intervals. Since household expenditure is subject to seasonal variations, the field work was extended over a full year; and the sample was chosen carefully so that it would be representative of all geographical areas and all social classes in the country. Many of the households which were approached could not provide the necessary information, but budgets were obtained from nearly 13,000 households.

It was found that the expenditure patterns of the wealthiest and poorest sections of the community differed considerably from the rest: they were therefore excluded from the analysis. The wealthiest group was defined as those households in which the chief wage-earner earned more than £20 per week; they accounted for 3½ per cent of the sample. At the other end of the income scale were those households which were mainly dependent on National Insurance Retirement Pensions, National Assistance Payments or similar forms of income: this group formed 6½ per cent of the sample. The weighting system for the new Retail Price Index was therefore derived from the expenditure pattern of the remaining nine-tenths of the households.

The number of priced commodities was increased to 350 and among the new items included in the index were lard, quick frozen peas, dog biscuits, car licenses and the cost of luggage in advance. Changes were made in the grouping of the items and the number of main groups was increased to ten. But the most significant change was that the index ceased to be a working class price index: the index now measures changes in the prices of goods and services bought by nine-tenths of the households in this country, including the households of small and medium salary earners.

Lastly it is necessary to consider the problem of linking different series of index numbers. For the years 1938–55 three official indices of retail prices are available for the periods 1938 to June 1947, June 1947 to January 1952 and January 1952 to January 1956. One method of linking such series is simply to transform the data for the later period to a new scale using the end value of the earlier series as a starting point. This method can be used to link the series which was begun in January 1952 with the earlier series calculated with 1947 as base. Here is an example:

Index for August 1954 (January 1952 = 100) = 108·4
Index for January 1952 (June 1947 = 100) = 132·6
∴ Index for August 1954 (June 1947 = 100)

$$= \frac{108 \cdot 4 \times 132 \cdot 6}{100}$$

$$= 143 \cdot 7$$

Since this method makes no allowance for changes in the weighting system, it must be regarded as approximate: it should not be used to link essentially different index numbers such as the Cost of Living Index and the Interim Index of Retail Prices. In this case it is necessary to recalculate the index for 1938 using 1947 weights and commodities. Calculations of this kind have been made by Prof. R. G. D. Allen;[*] he concluded that the increase in retail prices during the years 1938–47 was of the order of 60 per cent, although the Cost of Living Index showed an increase of about 30 per cent in the same period.

The choice of base date is important. Diagram 7.2. shows changes in the all items index and the index for food prices for the eight years 1948–55 using both 1938 and 1947 as base years. From both graphs it is clear that food prices have risen faster than the average

* Allen R.G.D. Prices. London and Cambridge Economic Service Bulletin Vol. XXVII February 1949.

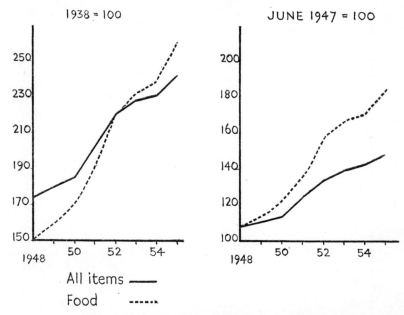

DIAGRAM 7.2   *Indices of Retail Prices 1948–55.*

*Source of data: London and Cambridge Economic Service
Bulletin and the Ministry of Labour Gazette.*

for all prices in these years, but the first graph shows that in the years 1938–47 food prices had lagged behind other prices: they did not catch up until some time in 1952, and by 1955 the food price index was only a few points above the all items index. The second graph using 1947 as a starting point ignores war-time changes: it only shows the greater than average increase in food prices during the years after 1947, and so shows a larger estimate of the difference between the two indices in 1955.

Although changes in the construction of the index introduced in January 1956 involved some changes in the commodities included in the index and their allocation to the main groups, the all items index may be linked to the earlier series by the simple method described above.

Any comparison of the changes in retail prices for the whole period 1913–1957 must involve a considerable amount of approxi-

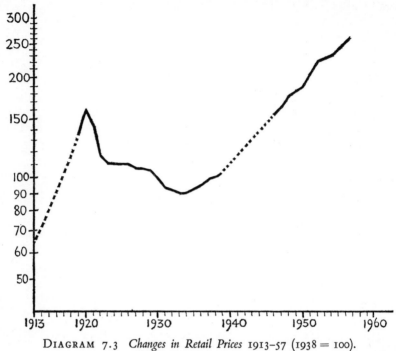

DIAGRAM 7.3   *Changes in Retail Prices 1913–57* (1938 = 100).
Source of data: London and Cambridge Economic Service Bulletin.

mation since the method of constructing the retail price index has
changed greatly in this period. Nevertheless such a series is useful
for making a comparison of the course of inflation during and after
the two world wars. It is shown on a logarithmic scale in Diagram
7.3. Inflation has been a slower process in the later period, but it has
also been more prolonged.

ADDENDUM

There have been further changes in the Retail Price Index since these
notes were written. The most important of these changes involves
an annual revision of the weighting system using data derived from
the Family Expenditure Survey which has been made continuously
since January 1957. A new weighting system derived from survey
data for July 1958—June 1961 was introduced in January 1962 for

use in that year and the indices so calculated have been linked to the index with base date January 1956 by the method described above. For 1963 a new set of weights will be derived from the survey data for July 1959—June 1962 and these indices will be linked to the index for January 1962 as part of a new series of Retail Price Indices with that date as base date.

Details of these and other changes are given in a *Report on Revision of the Index of Retail Prices* (Cmnd 1657) and the *Ministry of Labour Gazette* for March 1962.

September 1962

RECOMMENDED READING

'Method of Construction and Calculation of the Index of Retail Prices', *Studies in Statistical Methods No. 6.* H. M. S. O., (pamphlet) 1959.

Report on Proposals for a New Index of Retail Prices, Cmd. 9710. H. M. S. O., 1956.

Report of the Advisory Committee on the working of the Interim Index of Retail Prices, Cmd. 8481. H. M. S. O., 1952.

Interim Report of the Cost of Living Advisory Committee, Cmd. 7077. H. M. S. O., 1947.

Report of Enquiry into Household Expenditure in 1953-4, Ministry of Labour. H. M. S. O., 1957.

CHAPTER 8

PRICE AND VOLUME INDICES

INDEX numbers are used to measure changes over time or place. The term can be applied to any indirect measurement. The Retail Price Index and the Comparative Mortality Index have been described in earlier chapters. There are indices of production, traffic density, social mobility, adverse social conditions and many others. The method of calculation of these indices varies according to the nature of the phenomena for which they are required and many require statistical techniques which are outside the scope of this book.

It is convenient to begin by considering the construction of price indices which are both averages and percentages. The Retail Price Index is of this kind, and from the discussion of the last chapter, it is clear that three types of problem are involved, the choice of commodities to be included, the weighting system to be used and the base date from which the changes are to be measured.

The choice of base date determines which changes are included and which excluded from the index: and the level of prices at the base date fixes the scale on which these changes are measured. This choice is particularly important when two or more series of index numbers are to be compared; the use of different base-dates can lead to different conclusions since they involve essentially different comparisons. In the last chapter this point was illustrated by a comparison of the rise in food prices and in all retail prices in the post-war period.

The choice of commodities to be included in an index depends on both the practicability of obtaining a satisfactory price series for them and their importance for the purpose of the index. Some of the problems involved in the determination of suitable price series were considered in connection with the Retail Price Index. Another problem of this kind arises from the use of average values as prices: it occurs in the construction of indices of import and export prices.

All imports and exports are classified according to official lists and importers and exporters must declare both the value and the quantity of the goods imported or exported. The information obtained in this way is published in the Trade and Navigation Accounts of the

United Kingdom and is used for the indices of import and export prices which are published monthly by the Board of Trade.

The type of calculation involved in the construction of these indices is illustrated in Table 8.1. This gives the quantities and values of citrus fruit imported into the United Kingdom in 1953 and 1954 respectively. For each type of fruit it is possible to calculate the average value per 1000 cwt. of fruit each year: a price index may then be calculated using these average values as prices. The simplest method of calculating the index involves the comparison of the value of exports for 1953 at 1954 average values, with the declared values for 1953. The method is similar to that used in Table 7.1.

TABLE 8.1

INDICES OF IMPORT PRICES

Fruit	Quantities imported (000 cwts.)		Value of imports (£ 000)		Average values 1954 £ per cwt.	1953 imports at 1954 values £000
	1953	1954	1953	1954		
Clementines etc.	223	328	726	920	2·805	626
Sweet Oranges	7,761	6,891	17,345	17,118	2·484	19,278
Bitter Oranges	397	335	812	667	1·991	790
Grape-fruit	1,003	1,044	2,599	2,971	2·846	2,855
Lemons and Limes	586	575	1,740	1,921	3·341	1,958
Totals			23,222	23,597		25,507

Source of data: Trade of the U.K. 1955 Vol. 1.

$$\text{Price Index 1954 (1953} = 100) = \frac{25,507 \times 100}{23,222}$$

$$= 110.$$

Many imports are raw materials which are specified in detail and for these average values will be equivalent to prices. But the average values of some manufactured articles will reflect changes in the type of article imported as well as changes in price. For example, the average value per hundredweight of potassium carbonate will be more akin to a price than the average value of the motor vehicles or clocks imported in any time period. When choosing commodities for inclusion in the indices of import and export prices, the Board of Trade find it necessary to consider both their importance to international trade and the extent to which changes in their average values can be regarded as reliable indicators of price changes.

The weighting system for a price index is generally determined by the values of the commodities which are bought or sold. These values also vary with time and it is important to distinguish between weighting systems which are derived from purchases in the base year and those whose weighting systems are derived from purchases in the current year. These two types of index may be described thus:

$$\text{Base weighted index} = \frac{\text{Cost of commodities bought in base year at current year prices.}}{\text{Actual cost of commodities bought in base year}}$$

$$\text{Currently weighted index} = \frac{\text{Actual cost of commodities bought in current year}}{\text{Cost of same commodities at base year prices}}$$

They are known as Laspeyre and Paasche indices respectively. These ratios must, of course, be expressed as percentages, and it is convenient to write them algebraically.

Suppose quantities q_0, q_0', q_0'', ... of a set of commodities are bought at prices p_0, p_0', p_0'', ... in the base year, year 0 and that quantities q_1, q_1', q_1'', ... of these same commodities are bought at prices p_1, p_1', p_1'', ... in the current year, year 1. Then the values of these two sets of commodities can be obtained by multiplying the p's and q's, i.e. they will be p_0q_0, $p_0'q_0'$, $p_0''q_0''$, ... and p_1q_1, $p_1'q_1'$, $p_1''q_1''$, ... respectively. Also the aggregate value of base year commodities at year 1 prices will be Σp_1q_0 and the total cost of year 1 commodities at base year prices will be Σp_0q_1. The Laspeyre and Paasche price indices may therefore be written

$$\text{Price Index (Laspeyre)} = \frac{\Sigma p_1q_0}{\Sigma p_0q_0} \times 100$$

$$\text{Price Index (Paasche)} = \frac{\Sigma p_1q_1}{\Sigma p_0q_1} \times 100$$

TABLE 8.2
STATIONERY PRICES AND SALES 1954 AND 1957

Article	Prices at January		Quantities sold	
	1954	1957	1953/4	1956/7
	s. d	s. d	*number*	*number*
Ring files 1″ quarto	5. 5	6. 8	296	384
Lace files quarto	3. 0	3. 9	168	224
Wallets quarto	10	9	749	988
Paper quarto lined per ¼ ream	3. 3	3. 9	754	914
Ink — per bottle	1. 3	1. 3	284	234
	p_0	p_1	q_0	q_1

1954 sales at 1954 prices $= \Sigma p_0 q_0 = 66444$ pence
1957 ,, ,, 1954 ,, $= \Sigma p_0 q_1 = 82060$,,
1954 ,, ,, 1957 ,, $= \Sigma p_1 q_0 = 76171$,,
1957 ,, ,, 1957 ,, $= \Sigma p_1 q_1 = 94332$,,

Price Indices

$$\text{Laspeyre} = \frac{\Sigma p_1 q_0}{\Sigma p_0 q_0} \times 100 \qquad \text{Paasche} = \frac{\Sigma p_1 q_1}{\Sigma p_0 q_1} \times 100$$

$$= \frac{76171}{66444} \times 100 \qquad\qquad = \frac{94332}{82060} \times 100$$

$$= 114 \cdot 6 \qquad\qquad\qquad = 115 \cdot 0$$

The calculation of both types of index is illustrated in Table 8.2. These data relate to the prices and quantities of certain important items of stationery bought by Leicester University students during the sessions 1953–54 and 1956–57. Both indices show a marked increase in stationery prices in this period: though not identical, these indices have the same value when expressed to the nearest whole number.

Generally, the Laspeyre index is considered preferable to the Paasche index, since the use of constant weights means that each index is comparable with every other index in the series. If a Paasche formula is used, the weights change each year, and each index is strictly comparable only with that for the base year. Often however, there is no choice. In many practical problems, the available data will only be sufficient for the calculation of one type of index number.

Differences in the numerical values of the Laspeyre and Paasche indices, when they exist, are due to differences in the weighting systems. For short term comparisons, these differences are likely to be very small, as in the case of the stationery prices quoted above. But changes in economic conditions generally involve changes in the weights and under these circumstances the numerical difference between the indices may be considerable. For example, when prices are rising, purchasers may choose to buy more of those goods whose prices have risen less than average and less of those goods whose prices have risen to a greater extent. Under these circumstances, the Paasche index which takes account of the process of substitution will be lower than the Laspeyre index which does not.

An example of this type of change can be given from the Board of Trade price index for basic materials used in the non-food manufacturing industries. This index was begun in 1951: it uses a Laspeyre formula and the weights for the original index were calculated from the importance of the various basic materials as shown by the 1948 Census of Production. This index was revised in January 1958 and a new weighting system was introduced using data from the 1954 Census of Production. Among the reasons put forward for this change was the difference between the Laspeyre and Paasche indices for these prices at December 1954. These indices referred to June 1949 as base were 146·4 and 140·4 respectively:* owing to changes in the pattern of industrial production, the weighting system had become out of date, and the Laspeyre index exaggerated the increase in prices.

Similar problems arise in the comparison of prices in different countries. For example, in 1950 there could be no doubt that retail prices in the United Kingdom were lower than those in the United States, but the extent of the difference depended on the method used to measure it. A weighting system derived from the American pattern of expenditure showed that prices in the United Kingdom were approximately 20 per cent less than in the United States: but if the weighting system were derived from the United Kingdom pattern of expenditure, the difference was roughly 40 per cent.**

Two other types of index can be calculated from the complete

* Phillips, H. S.   U.K. Indices of Wholesale Prices, *Journal of the Royal Statistical Society*, Series A (General) 1956.
** Gilbert, M., and Kravis, I. B.: An International Comparison of Products and the Purchasing Power of Currencies, O.E.E.C., 1954.

price-quantity data assumed known above: they are indices of value and volume.

Value indices are extremely simple: they are the ratios of the values of the commodities bought at the two dates.

$$\text{i.e. Value Index} = \frac{\Sigma \, p_1 q_1}{\Sigma \, p_0 q_0} \times 100$$

There can only be one value index.

Volume indices measure changes in quantity, such as the quantity of food consumed or the output of an industry. It is generally impossible to measure such changes directly since Σq would be meaningless because of the variety of units of measurement involved. Numbers of eggs cannot be added to pints of milk or pounds of bread. One way of overcoming this difficulty is to take the ratio of the values of two sets of quantities at constant prices. As either the prices of the base year or the prices of the current year can be used for this calculation, there will be two volume indices to correspond to the two price indices.

$$\text{Volume Index (L)} = \frac{\Sigma \, p_0 q_1}{\Sigma \, p_0 q_0} \times 100$$

$$\text{Volume Index (P)} = \frac{\Sigma \, p_1 q_1}{\Sigma \, p_1 q_0} \times 100$$

Quantity or volume indices can also be obtained by dividing a value index by a price index: in this case, if a Laspeyre price index is used, the volume index will be of the Paasche type and vice-versa.

$$\frac{\text{Volume Index (L)}}{100} = \frac{\Sigma \, p_0 q_1}{\Sigma \, p_0 q_0} = \frac{\Sigma \, p_1 q_1}{\Sigma \, p_0 q_0} \times \frac{\Sigma \, p_0 q_1}{\Sigma \, p_1 q_1}$$

$$= \frac{\text{Value Index}}{\text{Price Index (P)}}$$

$$\frac{\text{Volume Index (P)}}{100} = \frac{\Sigma \, p_1 q_1}{\Sigma \, p_1 q_0} = \frac{\Sigma \, p_1 q_1}{\Sigma \, p_0 q_0} \times \frac{\Sigma \, p_0 q_0}{\Sigma \, p_1 q_0}$$

$$= \frac{\text{Value Index}}{\text{Price Index (L)}}$$

The data of Table 8.2. may be used to obtain a value index and two volume indices for the stationery purchased in 1956-7 referred to 1953-4 as base year.

$$\text{Value Index} = \frac{\Sigma p_1 q_1}{\Sigma p_0 q_0} \times 100 = \frac{94332 \times 100}{66444}$$

$$= 142 \cdot 0$$

$$\text{Volume Index (L)} = \frac{\Sigma p_0 q_1}{\Sigma p_0 q_0} \times 100 = \frac{82060 \times 100}{66444}$$

$$= 123 \cdot 5$$

$$\text{Volume Index (P)} = \frac{\Sigma p_1 q_1}{\Sigma p_1 q_0} \times 100 = \frac{94332 \times 100}{76171}$$

$$= 123 \cdot 8$$

Considering the three types of index together it may be seen that the increase of 42 per cent in stationery sales was due to a price increase of 15 per cent and an increase in the quantity of stationery sold of 24 per cent.

The data of Table 8.3. have been taken from the official estimates of National Income and Expenditure. It gives estimates of the total personal expenditure on food in the United Kingdom for the years 1948–54 at the prices actually paid in those years ($\Sigma p_1 q_1$) together with estimates of the cost of those same foodstuffs at 1948 prices ($\Sigma p_0 q_1$). The difference between these two estimates for any one year is a measure of the changes due to rising prices and the ratio of the two estimates provides a price index of the Paasche type. The same data may also be used to obtain value and volume indices for food consumption. The value indices have been obtained by expressing the estimates of expenditure at current prices in each year as a percentage of the expenditure in 1948, i.e. they have been derived from the data of column 2. The volume indices which are Laspeyre indices were obtained in the same way from column 3. Considering these two series along with the price indices of column 4, it is clear that the very considerable rise in expenditure on food during the years 1948–55 was largely due to increases in prices, though there was also some increase in the volume of consumption. Prices rose by 57

TABLE 8.3

FOOD PRICES AND FOOD CONSUMPTION U.K. 1948–55

Year	Personal Expenditure at current prices £m.	Personal Expenditure valued at 1948 prices £m.	Price Index (P) $(2 \div 3)$	Volume Index (L) from (3)	Value Index from (2)	Retail Price Index (L)
(1)	(2)	(3)	(4)	(5)	(6)	(7)
1948	2,265 $(\Sigma p_0 q_0)$	2,265 $(\Sigma p_0 q_0)$	100	100	100	100
1949	2,471 $(\Sigma p_1 q_1)$	2,364 $(\Sigma p_0 q_1)$	105	104	109	105
1950	2,734	2,449	112	108	121	113
1951	2,981	2,446	122	108	132	126
1952	3,282	2,421	136	107	145	145
1953	3,572	2,509	142	111	158	153
1954	3,842	2,599	148	115	170	157
1955	4,136	2,627	157	116	183	169

Source of data: Monthly Digest of Statistics.

per cent, consumption by 16 per cent and expenditure by 83 per cent in these seven years.

The Retail Price Index for these same years is shown in column 7: it may be compared with the consumer prices index calculated for column 4. In this case the Paasche index shows a smaller rise in prices than the Laspeyre index: but the difference between these indices is not entirely due to the use of different formulæ: the expenditure estimates cover a wider range of foodstuffs than the retail price index, and consequently are less affected by the removal of food subsidies in these years.

One of the most important volume indices published regularly by the government is the monthly Index of Industrial Production. This index is designed to measure month to month changes in average weekly production in the United Kingdom. For the purpose of this index, industrial production is defined as the work done by the mining, quarrying, manufacturing and building and contracting industries, together with the work done by the public utilities, gas, electricity and water. Each industry within this group obtains materials and services from other industries, and uses them to make its own products which may either be sold to the final consumer, or to other industries for use in their production. The work done by each industry can therefore be measured by the difference between the value of its output and the input needed to produce it. These values must, of course, be measured at constant prices. Information concerning these totals is generally only available annually from the Census of Production: consequently the formula described above cannot be used for this index. The alternative methods used for its construction will not be described here. It is sufficient to note that this index is a Laspeyre type index, whose weighting system reflects the importance of each industry, or section of each industry as measured by its contribution to total production in the base year 1954.

The choice of a Laspeyre or Paasche formula is just as important for volume indices as it is for price indices. The prices of products of expanding industries generally fall more or rise less than the prices of products of declining industries, consequently a Laspeyre index usually shows a greater increase in production than a Paasche index for the same period. For example, indices have been calculated to measure changes in production between 1935, the latest pre-war year and 1948, the first post-war year for which complete census of production data are available. The Laspeyre index using 1935 weights shows an increase of 40 per cent: the Paasche index using 1948 weights shows an increase of only 28 per cent.* The difference in this case is large, but this is only to be expected as there were many important changes in industry during the thirteen years between the two censuses.

Another volume index of considerable practical importance is an index of real wages, but before such an index can be considered, it is necessary to describe the indices of earnings and wage rates at present published by the Ministry of Labour.

The word wages has no precise statistical meaning, but the terms earnings and wage rates are used to describe two important aspects of wages. The total amount of money earned by an operative during a week or other fixed period is known as his earnings: it includes the National Insurance contribution and income tax, if any, which are deducted by the employer. The piece-rates, time-rates or bonus

* Brown, B. C., Industrial Production in 1935 and 1948, L.C.E.S., *Times Review of Industry*, December 1954.

systems used to calculate these earnings are known as wage-rates. Both types of information can be used to calculate indices showing changes in wages over a period of time, though the two types of index may behave very differently.

The indices of earnings and wage-rates which are given in Table 8.4. have been taken from reports of enquiries made by the Ministry of Labour concerning the earnings and hours of work of manual workers in a wide range of industries. These enquiries are made at six-monthly intervals in April and October each year. During the ten years 1947–1957 earnings rose more rapidly than wage-rates, though the difference in the rate of change was less marked at the end of this period than at the beginning.

The wage rate index is essentially a price index: it measures changes in the average cost of a normal week's work by a fixed labour force, i.e. a labour force with a constant age and sex composition and industrial distribution. The earnings index resembles a value index: it measures changes in the average earnings of a changing labour force working a variable week. Average weekly earnings are largely determined by wage-rates, but they are influenced by a number of

TABLE 8.4

EARNINGS AND WAGE-RATES: ALL WORKERS 1947-57

Date	Average Weekly earnings s. d.	Indices	
		Earnings	Wage-rates
April 1947	103. 6	100	100
„ 1948	114. 0	110	104
„ 1949	119. 4	115	108
„ 1950	124. 1	120	109
„ 1951	136. 2	132	119
„ 1952	147. 3	142	129
„ 1953	157. 7	152	136
„ 1954	166. 6	161	142
„ 1955	182. 3	176	152
„ 1956	197. 9	191	165
„ 1957	204. 7	198	169

Source of data: Ministry of Labour Gazette.

additional factors. Among these other factors are changes in the amount of overtime or short time worked: the movement of workers from the less well paid to the better paid industries: the up-grading of workers within the same industry and payments made above standard rates which may be made when labour is scarce. Changes in the proportions of workers engaged on piece-work and time work can also affect average earnings since it is usual for workers to earn more on piece-rates than time-rates when working on the same job. Also since average earnings for men are higher than average earnings for women and these in turn are higher than average earnings for juveniles, changes in the proportion of men, women and juveniles in the labour force will affect the average earnings of all workers. All these factors have been important since 1947, though some have been more important in some years than others.

The Ministry of Labour also publish a monthly index of wage-rates which covers more industries than the earnings enquiry: it includes coal-miners, agricultural workers and dock labourers who are excluded from the other enquiry. For the post-war years indices are available with base dates June 1947 and January 1956.

TABLE 8.5

INDICES OF WAGE-RATES AND PRICES. 1950–60
(JUNE 1947 = 100)

Year	Index of wage rates	Index of retail prices	Index of real wage rates
1950	110	114	96
1951	120	125	96
1952	130	136	96
1953	136	140	97
1954	142	143	99
1955	151	149	101
1956	163	156	104
1957	172	162	106
1958	178	167	107
1959	183	168	109
1960	187	169	111

Source of data: Monthly Digest of Statistics.

Since wages are useful for what they will buy, it is often necessary to consider changes in both wages and prices in the same period. It is generally sufficient to compare the two series of index numbers calculated from the same base date: occasionally however it may be desirable to combine these indices to give an index of real wages. Such an index is a volume index: it measures changes in the quantity of a fixed assortment of goods and services which can be bought with weekly wages in the period for which it is calculated. Such indices may measure changes in either real earnings or real wage-rates.

An index of real wage-rates for the years 1950–60 is shown in Table 8.5, together with the indices of wage-rates and retail prices from which it has been calculated. All three indices measure changes from June 1947. During the early years of this decade the wage-rate index lagged behind the price index, but the opposite was true for the years 1955–60.

Recommended Reading

Carter, C. F., Reddaway, W. B., and Stone R. 'The Measurement of Production Movements'. University of Cambridge Department of Applied Economics Monograph No. 1. Cambridge University Press 1948.

'Council on Prices, Productivity and Incomes'. First Report 1958. H. M. S. O.

Ulmer, M. J. *The Economic Theory of Cost of Living Price Index Numbers*, Columbia University Press, New York, 1949.

CHAPTER 9

THE ANALYSIS OF TIME SERIES

THE graph of household expenditure on food which is shown in Diagram 9.1. is typical of many economic time series. It shows average weekly expenditure per head for the years 1952–55. This graph moves up and down over the period shown, but this movement is not entirely irregular: it suggests a recurring pattern. Also if these fluctuations are ignored, there is a general tendency for the graph to move upward during the whole period.

It is convenient to regard the up and down movement in any graph such as this as being composed of three distinct types of movement, superimposed on each other. These three types of movement are:

    (i)   a long term trend
    (ii)   a short term regular variation
    (iii) a random fluctuation.

For the meanings of these terms it is useful to consider the graphs of Diagram 9.2. Graph A shows the average weekly earnings of adult men in a wide range of industries: it consists of an almost smooth line, i.e. this series is almost entirely long term trend. Graph B. is plotted from quarterly data. It shows the number of passenger journeys originating on British Railways during each quarter. Over the period as a whole, the graph shows little tendency to either increase or decrease, but the pattern of movement within one year is repeated more or less exactly in other years. In this case the regular variation is seasonal, but short term regular variation can also be related to days in the week, or hours of the day, e.g. domestic consumption of electricity or gas would show both these types of variation as well as seasonal variation. Graph C. shows the number of workers involved in strikes or industrial stoppages each month. There is little pattern in this series, which has a large random component.

The graph of household expenditure on food shows all three types of movement. The upward trend over the whole period is

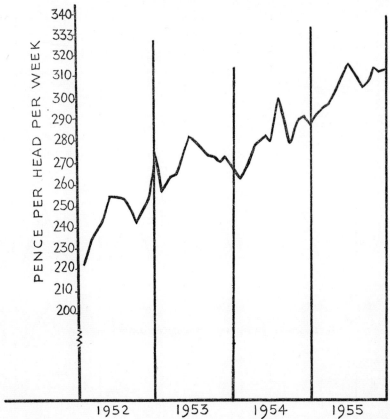

DIAGRAM 9.1 *Expenditure on Food — all households 1952–55, Monthly Averages.*
Source of data: Domestic Food Consumption and Expenditure
1955: Annual Report of the National Food Survey
Committee.

largely due to the increase in food prices which occurred in these
years, though there was also some increase in the quantity of food
consumed. Food rationing was finally brought to an end in 1954
and many non-rationed foods also became more plentiful in this
period.

Expenditure on food shows a marked seasonal variation. The
maximum within the year usually occurs in May or June. At this
time of year the previous season's fruit and vegetables are becoming
scarce, and the new ones are rather expensive. As they come on to

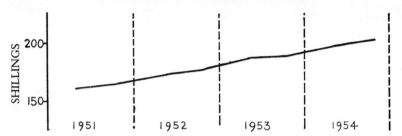

A. Average weekly earnings of men (21+) in Great Britain.

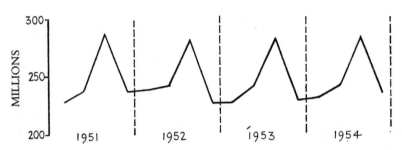

B. Passenger journeys originating on British Railways.

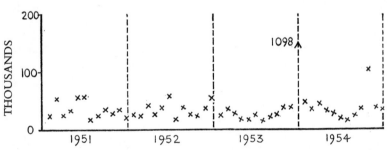

C. Number of workers involved in industrial stoppages in the U.K.

DIAGRAM 9.2 *Examples of Time Series.*
Source of data: Monthly Digest of Statistics.

the market, household expenditure on food tends to increase. A secondary peak might be expected in December, owing to Christmas expenditure. This is not shown in the graph except for 1952. It is possible that some of this expenditure is incurred in the previous month, but the method of taking the survey is also partly responsible. Information is obtained from a sample of households each of which keeps a log-book, but they are not expected to do this during the Christmas holiday.

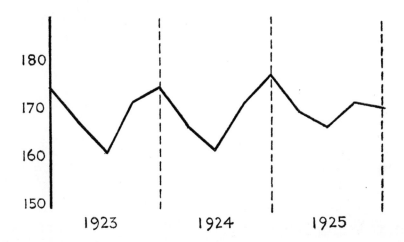

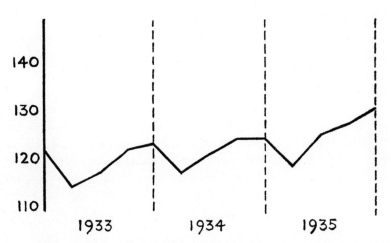

DIAGRAM 9.3   *Seasonal Variation in Food Prices* (1914 = 100).
Source of data: The Cost of Living Index, Ministry of Labour Gazette.

The seasonal pattern is not identical from one year to the next. These variations which may be regarded as random, may be due to the weather causing an early or late crop of a particular kind or to changes in the rationing scheme. The peak month for 1954 was July when rationing ended, and not May or June as in the other years.

It is often useful to assess the relative importance of these three types of movement, using an elementary analysis to separate them. Such an analysis should be used with caution since it involves the assumption that these three types of movement are independent and that the seasonal pattern is constant over time. In practice these assumptions are never entirely justified. A large random variation is likely to affect the trend: passengers who find other means of getting to work during a bus or railway strike, may continue to use them when the strike is over. Also much economic activity is designed to modify the seasonal pattern: farmers try to avoid too great a seasonal variation in the production of milk: any full employment policy aims at reducing seasonal unemployment. Diagram 9.3. showing changes in food prices at different periods illustrates the fact that seasonal patterns may change in the course of time.

One of the most useful methods of determining the trend in a time series is the method of moving averages.

To find a moving average it is necessary to take the first few terms of the series, say the first three, shown as A, B, C, in Diagram 9.4. and find their arithmetic mean. This average is shown as X: it gives the trend value for a point of time corresponding to the second observation, B. Next the average of the second set of three observations, B, C, D is taken. Their average, shown as Y, gives the trend value for a point of time corresponding to C and so on. If the moving average is made for an odd number of observations, then the trend values refer to the same point in time as an observation of the original series. If the moving average is taken for an even number of observations, then the trend value corresponds to a point in time halfway between two of the original observations. In most cases this would be inconvenient: consequently a second moving average of two terms is also taken.

If the trend series can be represented by a straight line, a moving average will leave the trend unchanged, but this method of analysis

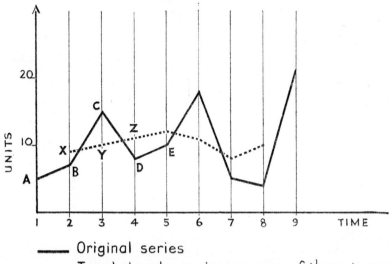

Original series

Trend given by moving average of three terms

DIAGRAM 9.4   *A Moving Average.*

distorts a curved trend to some extent. The regular variation will be
eliminated if the number of terms used for the moving average is
the same as the number of terms in the period covered by this regular
variation: i.e. a four quarterly moving average removes the seasonal
variation from quarterly data, and a twelve monthly moving average
removes the seasonal variation from monthly data. The moving
average also tends to smooth out the random variations. These
variations can be either positive or negative and in the long run must
average to zero: it is however unlikely that they will be completely
eliminated by taking a short term moving average.

The calculation of moving averages is illustrated in Tables 9.1.
and 9.2.

The data of Table 9.1. relate to the number of lunches served in a
college refectory for five weeks of an autumn term. These data show
some regular variation within the week: fewest lunches are served
on Wednesday: more lunches are served on Tuesday than Monday
and more on Thursday than Friday, but it is clear that in any week
this pattern may be changed by random events: e.g. the weather,
a sports event at home or away, an important meeting or lecture.

TABLE 9.1

CALCULATION OF A MOVING AVERAGE
(ODD NUMBER OF TERMS)

Day	Number of lunches served	Add in fives	Divide by 5 Trend
Monday	378		
Tuesday	359		
Wednesday	321	1757	351
Thursday	371	1725	345
Friday	328	1730	346
Monday	346	1767	353
Tuesday	364	1743	349
Wednesday	358	1756	351
Thursday	347	1757	351
Friday	341	1749	350
Monday	347	1692	338
Tuesday	356	1669	334
Wednesday	301	1642	328
Thursday	324	1596	319
Friday	314	1587	317
Monday	301	1570	314
Tuesday	347	1586	317
Wednesday	284	1574	315
Thursday	340	1578	316
Friday	302	1552	310
Monday	305	1552	310
Tuesday	321	1535	307
Wednesday	284	1523	305
Thursday	323		
Friday	290		

Data relate to number of lunches served in college refectory each day for five weeks.

Table 9.2. shows personal expenditure on travel in the United Kingdom for the years 1951–4. The seasonal variation shown by these data is similar to that of Diagram 9.2. B, but it is rather more marked. Expenditure on travel is highest in the third and lowest in the first quarter of each year. The trend has been found by taking a moving average of four terms followed by a moving average of two terms. Both the original series and the trend are shown in Diagram 9.5.

TABLE 9.2
CALCULATION OF TREND AND ESTIMATE OF SEASONAL VARIATION

Data relate to Personal Expenditure on Travel in the U.K. and have been taken from the Monthly Digest of Statistics. Units £million throughout.

Expenditure			Add in Fours	Add in Pairs	Divide by 8 Ttrend	Deviation from Trend	Estimate Seasonal Variation	Seasonally Corrected Series
1951	1	76					− 17·61	93·61
	2	97					+ 2·81	94·14
	3	122	384	776	97·000	+ 25·000	+ 25·22	96·78
	4	89	392	793	99·125	− 10·125	− 10·40	99·40
1952	1	84	401	810	101·250	− 17·250	− 17·61	101·61
	2	106	409	824	103·000	+ 3·000	+ 2·81	103·19
	3	130	415	836	104·500	+ 25·500	+ 25·22	104·78
	4	95	421	848	106·000	− 11·000	− 10·40	105·40
1953	1	90	427	859	107·375	− 17·375	− 17·61	107·61
	2	112	432	869	108·625	+ 3·375	+ 2·81	109·19
	3	135	437	876	109·500	+ 25·500	+ 25·22	109·78
	4	100	439	878	109·750	− 9·750	− 10·40	110·40
1954	1	92	439	879	109·875	− 17·875	− 17·61	109·61
	2	112	440	883	110·375	+ 2·375	+ 2·81	109·19
	3	136	443				+ 25·22	110.78
	4	103					− 10·40	113·40

Quarters	1	2	3	4
			+ 25·000	− 10·125
	− 17·250	+ 3·000	+ 25·500	− 11·000
	− 17·375	+ 3·375	+ 25·500	− 9·750
	− 17·875	+ 2·375		
Totals	− 52·500	+ 8·750	+ 76·000	− 30·875
A.M.	− 17·50	+ 2·92	+ 25·33	− 10·29

Since the sum of these averages is + 0·46 deduct one quarter of this quantity from each.

| Seasonal variation | − 17·61 | + 2·81 | + 25·22 | − 10·40 |

The method of moving averages has two disadvantages: the arithmetic is often tedious and the trend can only be determined for a period of time which is one year less than that for which the original series is given. This second disadvantage is particularly important in

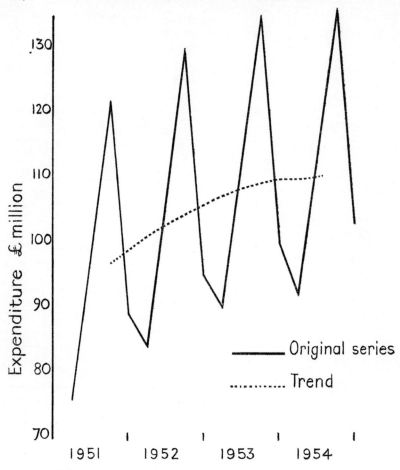

DIAGRAM 9.5   *Personal Expenditure on Travel in the U.K.*

the case of short series. Graphical methods can be used to overcome these difficulties, and they are particularly useful in a preliminary analysis which may be required quickly. The original series together with the annual averages should be drawn on a graph. A smooth line should then be drawn to fit the annual averages as nearly as possible and at the same time this line should indicate the general movement of the series.

Estimates of seasonal variation are obtained by averaging the quarterly deviations from the trend. These deviations are obtained by subtracting the trend values from the original series: they represent the sum of the regular and random variations present in the series. Averaging these deviations for each quarter separately reduces, though it may not entirely eliminate the random variation. If necessary, these averages are adjusted so that they add to zero.

If the trend has been determined by the method of moving averages, the calculation is made by the method illustrated in Table 9.2. If the trend has been determined graphically, the deviations of the original series from the trend can easily be read from the graph, and the calculation completed in the same way.

An alternative method of calculating seasonal variation is available for series for which the trend can be assumed linear. It does not involve determining the trend. The averages for each quarter are compared with the average for all observations and an adjustment is made for the trend. This method is illustrated in Table 9.3. where it has been applied to the travel expenditure data for the years 1951–53, during which the trend was approximately linear. In this case, both methods of estimating seasonal variation give very similar results.

In describing these calculations it has been assumed that the original series would consist of quarterly data showing seasonal variation. The same methods are, of course, applicable to monthly data, though series which are affected by variable holidays such as Easter and Whitsun may need special treatment. These methods could also be used to determine the daily variation within a week or the hourly variation within a day in suitable cases.

When comparisons are made over time, they can either be restricted to the same quarter or the same month of each year, or use can be made of a "seasonally corrected" series. Such a series is obtained by subtracting the seasonal variation from the original series to give a series which combines the trend and the random variations. For example, comparing travel expenditure in the third quarter of 1953 with that for the first quarter of 1954, it is clear that expenditure was very much lower at the second date, being only £92 million compared with £135. But the seasonally corrected series, also shown in Table 9.2. shows that this difference can be wholly explained by

TABLE 9.3

CALCULATIONS OF SEASONAL VARIATION FOR SERIES WITH LINEAR TREND

Quarters	I	2	3	4	Total	A.M.
1951	76	97	122	89	384	96·00
1952	84	106	130	95	415	103·75
1953	90	112	135	100	437	109·25
Totals	250	315	387	284	1236	103
A.M.	83·33	105	129	94·66	103	

Deviations from 103

   − 19·67   + 2·0   + 26·00   − 8·34

Adjustment for trend *

   − 2·49   − ·83   + ·83   + 2·49

Seasonal variation (subtract above figures)

   − 17·18   + 2·83   + 25·17   − 10·83

* Change mid 1951 to mid 1953 = 109·25 − 96·00
$$= 13·25$$
∴ Average change per quarter = 13·25 ÷ 8
$$= 1·66$$
∴ Adjustment for trend for 2nd and 3rd quarters
$$= \mp \tfrac{1}{2} \times 1·66 = \mp ·83$$
and Adjustment for trend for 1st and 4th quarters
$$= \mp 1\tfrac{1}{2} \times 1·66 = \mp 2·49·$$

the seasonal variation. Expenditure on travel had not fallen by more than was to be expected at that time of year.

Since July 1956, the Central Statistical Office has published a seasonally corrected series for the Index of Industrial Production.

The seasonal pattern in this index is rather complicated. Much of the increase in industrial production which occurs in any year appears to be concentrated in the autumn months. This may be partly the effect of summer holidays on the workers and partly the result of the overhauling of machinery and re-tooling the workshops which is frequently undertaken in those same holidays. Sickness tends to lower production at the beginning of the year: holidays reduce production at Christmas, Easter and Whitsun and are responsible for the very low rate of production in August. Production may also be affected by seasonal variations in the availability of raw materials and seasonal changes in the demand for various types of goods.

Since the seasonal pattern is complex, estimates of the seasonal variation in this index involve rather more complicated methods than those described above.

The index, as originally calculated, allows for variations in the number of days in the month: it does this by measuring changes in average weekly production. The seasonal correction is made in two stages. The effect of public holidays and annual holidays on the rate of production in different industries is estimated for each month and removed from the index. The remaining seasonal variation is then estimated by the method of moving averages.

Both the original series and the seasonally corrected series for the years 1954–57 are shown in Diagram 9.6. The latter provides a very useful indication of the trend in production.

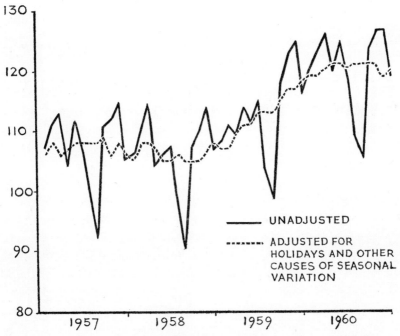

DIAGRAM 9.6   *The Index of Industrial Production 1957–60 (1954 = 100).*
Source of data: Monthly Digest of Statistics.

The seasonal pattern in any series is likely to change in the course of time. This is particularly important in the case of the index of industrial production which could be affected by changes in overseas trade, holidays, employment, and many other factors. The estimates of seasonal variation which have been made for this index will therefore be reviewed periodically.

The analysis of time series described here is only suitable for reasonably short series with marked regular variations. It is not adequate to deal with problems of long series involving irregular cyclical fluctuations, i.e. it is not adequate for trade cycle analysis. These methods can also be used as a first stage in the projection of economic time series, but any forecast of future values must be based on a detailed knowledge of the phenomena being measured as well as a knowledge of statistical techniques.

RECOMMENDED READING

'Seasonally adjusted quarterly estimates of income and expenditure', Economic Trends, January 1960.

'Seasonal Movements in Statistics of Unemployment and Unfilled Vacancies", Economic Trends, March 1960.

'The Index of Retail Prices', Economic Trends, May 1960.

II. 1 (a) According to information published in the *Ministry of Labour Gazette*, the average earnings for men engaged in the paper and printing industries was 273s. 9d. per week in October 1956. The corresponding average for men engaged in the textile industry was 218s. 9d. per week. Is it reasonable to suppose that Mr Smith who is a printer, was earning nearly £3 a week more than his neighbour, Mr Brown, who is a cotton weaver?

(b) The combined weight for drink and tobacco in the Interim Index of Retail Prices (June 1947 = 100) was 217. This was reduced to 151 in the new Retail Price Index which was begun in January 1956. Does this indicate that less money was spent on drink and tobacco in 1956 than in 1947?

II. 2. The following information concerning the food section of the Retail Price Index has been taken from the *Ministry of Labour Gazette*.

Food	Weight	Price Index, January 1958 (January 1956 = 100)
Bread, flour, cereals, biscuits and cake	52	119
Meat and bacon	89	99
Fish	9	119
Butter, margarine, lard and cooking fat	19	82
Milk, cheese and eggs	53	106
Tea, coffee, cocoa, soft drinks, etc.	22	102
Sugar, preserves, confectionery	39	98
Vegetables, fresh, dried and canned	33	110
Fruit, fresh, dried and canned	19	122
Other food	15	104

(i)   Calculate the total index for food at January, 1958.
(ii) Calculate an alternative price index suitable for use by vegetarians.

II. 3. Calculate a price index for imported bulbs in 1957 (1954 = 100.)

U.K. imports of bulbs. 1954 and 1957

| | Quantities (millions) | | Values (£000) | |
	1954	1957	1954	1957
Narcissi	74	64	829	803
Tulips	151	145	1,195	1,274
Hyacinths	22	26	552	631
Other	387	414	995	1,275
Total	634	649	3,571	3,983

Source: Trade of U.K. 1957. Vol. I.

II. 4.

Consumers' Expenditure on some items of food U.K. 1950–58 (£m)

| Year | At current prices | | | At 1954 prices | | |
	Bread and Cereals	Meat and Bacon	Fruit and Vegetables	Bread and Cereals	Meat and Bacon	Fruit and Vegetables
1950	437	529	449	527	797	527
1952	502	679	495	526	712	529
1954	467	850	571	467	850	571
1956	506	1,059	682	464	931	596
1958	557	1,122	764	461	955	615

Source: National Income and Expenditure 1960.

Use the above data to calculate price and volume indices for each of these types of food. Comment on the changes indicated by these index numbers.

II. 5. The Index of weekly wage-rates for January 1958 (January 1956 = 100) was 112·2. The value of this index for January 1956 (June 1947 = 100) was 156·1. Obtain an index measuring changes in weekly wage rates from June 1947 to January 1958.

Explain why this method of linking indices is only approximate.

II. 6. The county of Blankshire pay the head teachers of their schools a basic salary, together with an allowance which depends on the size of their school. Information concerning allowances and the size distribution of the county schools are given in the following table. The average allowance paid to head teachers was 78% higher in the second year than in the first. Determine to what extent this increase was due to increases in the scale of allowances and to what extent it was due to changes in the size-distribution of the schools.

Size of School No. of pupils	First year		Second year	
	Number of Schools	Head teachers allowance	Number of Schools	Head teachers allowance
Under 100	21	£ 80	16	£155
100–250	32	£140	32	£235
250–500	41	£220	39	£355
500–750	17	£360	21	£500
750 & over	4	£500	12	£750
Total or average	115	£202·6	120	£361·2

Imaginary data

II. 7. (a) "The fact that in 1957 the birth-rate in the New Towns was double the national average shows that, given the right environment, English people prefer to have larger families." Do you agree?

(b) "In 1955 the crude death rates for Japan and Sweden were 7.8 and 9.4 respectively." "Sweden is a much healthier country than Japan." Would you regard these statements as incompatible?

II.   8.   Draw a graph to illustrate the following time-series.

Index of vehicle miles travelled on roads in Great Britain: Pedal Cycles
(Monthly Average 1958 = 100)

	1958	1959	1960
January	79	65	59
February	74	72	67
March	86	89	88
April	106	98	90
May	117	110	103
June	121	115	107
July	122	126	99
August	117	123	99
September	107	112	91
October	103	93	81
November	84	79	74
December	84	70	62
Average of monthly values	100	96	85

Source: Monthly Digest of Statistics.

Draw a freehand trend to fit these data and use your graph to make a rough estimate of the seasonal variation in this series.

II.   9.   The following table shows the number of books which were returned each day to a University College Library in four weeks of a summer term.

Week	Monday	Tuesday	Wednesday	Thursday	Friday	Saturday
1	123	132	118	114	104	40
2	139	128	89	123	128	42
3	145	149	98	136	173	47
4	194	152	115	138	149	59

Use the method of moving averages to determine the trend in this series. Plot both the original series and the trend series on the same graph.

II.   10.

New Registrations of Motor cycles and tricycles
G.B. 1952–57

Year	Quarters			
	I	2	3	4
1952	33·1	41·4	39·5	21·8
1953	30·3	44·4	39·7	26·9
1954	35·0	52·9	47·8	33·1
1955	42·0	61·8	54·6	33·5
1956	36·0	47·0	34·6	30·3
1957	63·3	71·1	51·5	27·0

Source: Monthly Digest of Statistics.

Using the data for 1952–1955 only, obtain an estimate of the
seasonal variation in this series. Could these estimates be
used to obtain a seasonally corrected series for the years
1956 and 1957?

PART III

THE MEASUREMENT OF VARIATION

CHAPTER 10

FREQUENCY DISTRIBUTIONS AND AVERAGES

STATISTICS and statistical methods are not concerned with individuals as individuals, but with individuals as members of a group or population, and one of the most obvious characteristics of both natural and social groups is the variation between individuals of the same kind. Examples are hardly necessary: everyone is familiar with the differing heights and weights of men, the various incomes they receive and the sizes of the towns in which they live. Less obvious, but equally important, is the fact that this variation often conforms to a pattern. The next few chapters are concerned with methods of describing and measuring this variation between members of the same group.

Measurable characteristics are usually referred to as variables and it is convenient to distinguish between those which are discrete and those which are continuous. Continuous variables can take any value within a range: examples are heights, weights and ages. Discrete variables can only take particular values and in many cases can only take whole number values: the numbers of persons in a family or rooms in a house are of this type.

From a practical point of view, the distinction between discrete

TABLE 10.1

NUMBER OF ELECTORS PER ADDRESS IN WEST STREET

Number of voters	Number of addresses with this number of voters						
1.	XXX						3
2.	XXXXX	XXXXX	XXXXX	XXXXX	XXXXX	XXXXX ⎱	58
	XXXXX	XXXXX	XXXXX	XXXXX	XXXXX	XXX ⎰	
3.	XXXXX	XXXXX	XXXXX	X			16
4.	XXX						3
5 or more							—
			Total number of addresses				80

and continuous variables is not as simple as this. If the unit of measurement is small compared with the range of values to be considered, as for town populations, then a discrete variable must be treated as if it were continuous. On the other hand, since the accuracy with which continuous variables are measured is limited by the equipment available, and the units used, it will sometimes be convenient to treat them as discrete variables. In economic theory prices are often treated as continuous variables, but for retail prices the smallest unit available is the halfpenny and this is seldom used: also there are generally recognized conventions concerning what is and what is not a suitable price for particular types of commodities.

The numerical data obtained by measuring or counting a partic-

TABLE 10.2

HEIGHTS OF NATIONAL SERVICEMEN, 1939

Heights in inches	Number of recruits
Less than 58	53
58–59	75
59–60	126
60–61	402
61–62	981
62–63	2110
63–64	4036
64–65	7317
65–66	10519
66–67	13316
67–68	14159
68–69	12817
69–70	10256
70–71	7031
71–72	3914
72–73	2284
73–74	1134
74–75	439
75–76	120
76–77	46
77 or more	26

Source: W. J. Martin. The Physique of Young Adult Males.
M.R.C. Memo. No. 20.

ular characteristic for all members of a group can be arranged in a frequency table. An example of the construction of such a table for the case of a discrete variable with small integral values is given in Table 10.1. The data relate to the number of voters registered at each address in a particular street, and similar data can be obtained from any electoral register. The classes are those addresses with 1, 2, 3... voters. It is customary to construct the table making a cross or other mark opposite the appropriate class for each member of the group. If squared paper is used, the numbers of crosses are easily ascertained and can be entered in the last column.

In this street the maximum number of electors per address is four, so that there is no difficulty in allowing one class for each number of voters. In some examples of this type it may be necessary to group the higher classes.

For continuous variables, the choice of class interval may be more difficult. For most problems, it is desirable to have at least ten groups,

TABLE 10.3

SIZE DISTRIBUTION OF URBAN DISTRICTS IN ENGLAND AND WALES. 1951

Population	Number of Districts
Under 5,000	130
5,000–10,000	150
10,000–15,000	88
15,000–20,000	72
20,000–25,000	43
25,000–30,000	30
30,000–35,000	16
35,000–40,000	13
40,000–45,000	9
45,000–50,000	4
50,000–55,000	2
55,000–60,000	2
60,000–65,000	3
65,000–70,000	3
70,000–75,000	1
75,000 and over	6

Source: Census, 1951. England and Wales. General Tables.

since the use of too few groups results in the loss of useful information: on the other hand, the use of too many groups makes the tables unwieldy. Also, if possible, the class intervals should be equal, since this simplifies any calculations made on the data. Two examples of frequency tables are given in Tables 10.2 and 10.3. The first gives the heights of 91,163 National Servicemen who were medically examined in three months of 1939. The second shows the populations of English Urban Districts at the time of the 1951 Census.

It is important to note that no individual can belong to two classes. For these tables, the class intervals should read 58 inches but less than 59 inches and 5,000 but under 10,000 etc. It is usual to omit the words and give only the end values of the intervals as has been done here. The class intervals for urban district populations could have been written 5,000–9,999 etc. since this is a discrete variable.

Consideration of these tables shows that these distributions have very different shapes. The distribution of heights is more or less symmetrical: the largest frequencies are at the middle of the range and the end frequencies are relatively small. A great many men are

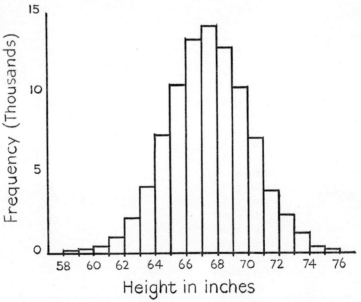

DIAGRAM 10.1   *Heights of National Servicemen, 1939.*

about average height and relatively few men are either very short or very tall. The distribution of town populations is much less symmetrical, or much more skew than the distribution of heights: the largest frequency is very near one end of the range, since small towns are far more numerous than large towns.

Frequency distributions may be represented graphically by means of histograms. These are a special form of bar chart, in which the heights of the rectangle are proportional to the frequency within unit range, and the areas of the rectangles are proportional to the frequency within the class intervals. If the class intervals are equal, all the rectangles will have the same width, but unequal class intervals will be represented by rectangles of unequal width.

Diagrams 10.1 and 10.2 give histograms for the data of Tables

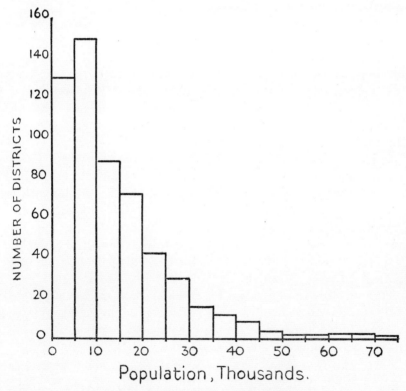

DIAGRAM 10.2 *Size Distribution of Urban Districts, England and Wales, 1951.*

10.2 and 10.3. The small classes at the ends of the distributions have been omitted from the diagrams. These histograms confirm the impressions already formed by a study of the tables. Both distributions are single humped distributions, but the distribution of town populations is skew whereas the distribution of heights is approximately symmetrical.

It is often impracticable to use equal intervals for highly skew distributions. Table 11.2. shows the distribution of personal incomes in the United Kingdom in 1954. In this case, the use of larger class intervals for the smaller incomes would change the shape of the distribution: instead of the highly skew distribution shown here, it would appear J-shaped, with the largest frequency at the beginning of the range. The use of smaller class intervals for the large incomes would make the table unmanageable.

Another example of the use of unequal class intervals is given in Table 10.4 and Diagram 10.3. These give the distribution of the salaries of University professors for the year 1946–47. In this case, the grouping appears more satisfactory than is actually the case. Both the frequency table and histogram suggest a smooth skew distribution but the actual distribution like many salary distributions for specific groups is better described as a step distribution. Of the 41 professors shown in the class £2,001–£2,500, 33 received salaries of £2,500 and it is possible that in some of the other classes there was a similar tendency for the values to bunch at one end of the interval.

When histograms are used to compare different distributions it is convenient to have either the same total frequency for each distribution, or to express the class frequencies as percentages of the total frequency. Diagram 10.4. shows the distributions of the weekly earnings of men in a number of industries in 1938, drawn from data giving percentage distributions.*

The distribution of earnings for all industries is more symmetrical than that for any individual group. It is also easy to see that average earnings in the paper and printing industries were higher than those in the public utilities or textile industries and that the first of these

* This information has been taken from R. B. Ainsworth, 'Earnings and Working Hours of Manual Wage Earners in the U.K. in October 1938.' *Journal Royal Statistical Society*, Series A (General) 1949. Similar information for October 1960 is now available in the *Ministry of Labour Gazette* for April 1961.

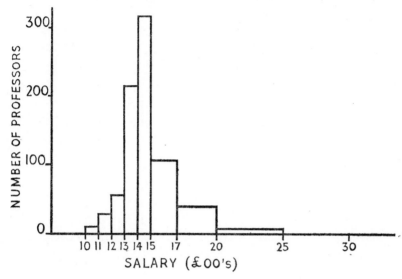

DIAGRAM 10.3   *Salaries of University Professors, 1946-47.*

industries had a particularly large proportion of men with relatively high earnings. The distribution of earnings in government industrial establishments has two humps: these presumably indicate two grades or two types of work for which different rates were paid.

Frequency distributions can be described in two ways. They can

TABLE 10.4

SALARIES OF UNIVERSITY PROFESSORS 1946-47

Range	Number of Professors
Up to and including £1000	16
£1001–£1100	8
£1101–£1200	28
£1201–£1300	55
£1301–£1400	215
£1401–£1500	318
£1501–£1700	217
£1701–£2000	119
£2001–£2500	41
£2501–£3000	1

Source: University Development 1935–47 H.M.S.O. 1948.

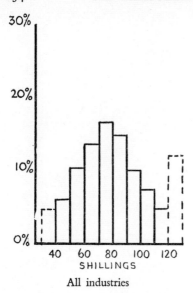

All industries

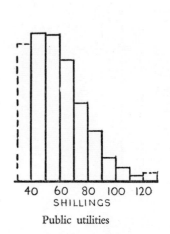

Public utilities

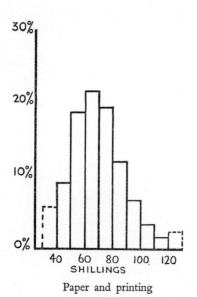

Paper and printing

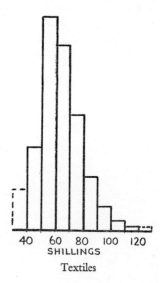

Textiles

DIAGRAM 10.4

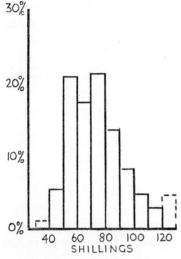

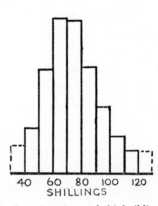

Government Industrial Establishments   Metal, engineering and shipbuilding

DIAGRAM 10.4 *Distribution of Weekly Earnings of Men* (21 +) *in Selected Industries in the U.K. at October* 1938.

either be compared with theoretical distributions which can be determined mathematically, or they can be described by a series of numerical characteristics or parameters.

When histograms have regular shapes it seems reasonable to fit curves to them and to use these curves to describe the frequency distributions. For example, the distribution of heights shown in Diagram 10.1. is approximately normal and this type of curve has been superimposed on the histogram in Diagram 12.2. As relatively few of the variables of economic and social statistics lend themselves to simple mathematical treatment it is generally more convenient to use parameters to describe these frequency distributions. The most generally used of these parameters are averages and measures of dispersion.

An average is a single measurement which in some way typifies the whole distribution. Several types of average are available, but of these the arithmetic mean, the median and the mode are the most useful.

The mean, or arithmetic mean, is simply the sum of all the values divided by the number of values. This average has been discussed in Chapter 6 and it is now only necessary to consider its calculation for grouped data. This calculation is similar to that for weighted averages, the weights in this case being the frequencies. An example is given in Table 10.5. It shows the calculation of the arithmetic mean height of 100 national servicemen: this distribution has been obtained by taking a random sample from the much larger population for which information is given in Table 10.2.

For the purposes of this calculation it is generally assumed that all values within a particular class have as mean the mid-value of that class. Such an assumption is not necessarily correct. It will usually be reasonable enough for the fairly large classes at the middle of the range, but may well be less accurate for the smaller classes at the ends of the distribution. If the distribution is fairly symmetrical, the errors at one end will more or less compensate for those at the other, and the error in the calculated value of the mean due to this assumption will be small. Such errors can however be serious in the case of very skew distributions or of step distributions: the methods described here should not be applied to the income distributions of Tables 11.2 or 10.4.

TABLE 10.5

CALCULATION OF ARITHMETIC MEAN (1)

(Data refer to heights of national servicemen)

Heights in inches	Number of men	Mid-value of interval ins.	Deviations from 68 ins.	Deviations $\div 2$ X	Product fX.
61–63	4	62	−6	−3	−12
63–65	12	64	−4	−2	−24
65–67	27	66	−2	−1	−27
67–69	32	68	0	0	0
69–71	16	70	+2	+1	+16
71–73	6	72	+4	+2	+12
73–75	3	74	+6	+3	+ 9
Total	100				−26

$$\text{Mean} = 68 - \frac{2 \times 26}{100} \text{ ins.}$$

$$= 67 \cdot 48 \text{ ins.}$$

Since it is assumed that the average value of the items within a class is equal to the mid-value of the class interval, the arithmetic mean for the whole distribution could be obtained by multiplying these mid-values by the frequencies and dividing by the total frequency. This is rarely done in practice, since much arithmetic can be saved by working in deviations from one of the mid-values expressed in terms of the class interval as unit.** In this case the deviations have been measured from 68 inches and divided by 2, since all the class intervals are of this size. The sum of the products of these deviations and frequencies is then averaged, multiplied back by the class interval

TABLE 10.6

CALCULATION OF ARITHMETIC MEAN (2)

Data relate to the weekly earnings of men (21 +) in the paper and printing industries. G.B. 1938.

Weekly earnings s.	Frequency per 1000 f.	Mid values s.	Deviations from 75 ÷ 10 X	fX
Under 40	46	35 *	− 4	− 184
40− 50	61	45	− 3	− 183
50− 60	101	55	− 2	− 202
60− 70	136	65	− 1	− 136
70− 80	165	75	0	0
80− 90	148	85	1	+ 148
90−100	100	95	2	+ 200
100−110	73	105	3	+ 219
110−120	48	115	4	+ 192
120 & over	122	135 *	6	+ 732
Totals	1000			+ 786

* It is likely that the 'over' group contains a wider range of earnings than the 'under' group: the mid-values for these groups have been taken as 35 and 135 respectively.

$$\text{Mean} = 75 + \frac{10 \times 786}{1000}$$
$$= 82.86s.$$

** If the use of deviations is not obvious, consider the problem of finding the average age of five children whose ages are 6 yrs. 2m: 6 yrs. 6 m: 6 yrs. 4m: 6 yrs. 2m and 6 yrs. 10 m. respectively. It is not necessary to add both the years and the months: the average must be 6 yrs. and a number of months and this number of months can be found by averaging the months only. Since all these ages involve an even number of months it would be possible to work in units of two months.

and added to the value from which the deviations were originally found.

The complete calculation is set out in Table 10.5., but not all these columns are necessary. The average height of the national servicemen found by this method is 67·48 inches.

The application of these methods to frequency distributions containing 'under' and 'over' groups presents extra difficulties. Where no lower or upper limit is given for the range, there can be no simple rule for fixing the mid-values of the end groups, and the assumptions made may or may not affect the accuracy with which the mean is calculated. The risk of a serious error is greater for skew than for symmetrical distributions and greater when these end groups form an appreciable proportion of the total frequency than when they do not. An example is given in Table 10.6. which shows the weekly earnings of men in the paper and printing industries in 1938: this table gives the data from which the histogram of Diagram 10.4. has been drawn. In this case it is possible to check the accuracy of the average calculated in this way since Mr Ainsworth's paper also gives an arithmetic mean calculated from the aggregate earnings for each industry. For the paper and printing industry this average was 84s. 3d: the error involved in this case is rather large, but this

TABLE 10.7

CALCULATION OF MEDIAN (1)

Data from Table 10.1.

Number of Electors	Number of Addresses	Cumulative frequency
1	3	3
2	58	61
3	16	77
4	3	80
5	—	—
Total	80	

$$\text{Median address} = \frac{n+1}{2} = \frac{81}{2} = 40 \cdot 5$$

This occurs in the second group

∴ Median number of electors = 2

TABLE 10.8
CALCULATION OF MEDIAN (2)
Data relate to heights of national servicemen

Height in ins.	Number of men	Cumulative frequency
61–63	4	4
63–65	12	16
65–67	27	43
67–69	32	75
69–71	16	91
71–73	6	97
73–75	3	100
Total	100	

$$\text{Median item} = \frac{100 + 1}{2} = 50\cdot5$$

This occurs in class interval 67–69 inches

$$\therefore \text{Median height} = 67 + \frac{\left(\frac{100}{2} - 43\right)}{32}$$

$$= 67\cdot44 \text{ ins.}$$

is not surprising since the 'under' and 'over' groups contain 17 per cent of the total frequency.

The second type of average to be considered is the median. The median can be defined as the value of the middle item when the items are arranged in order of size: it is therefore the value of the $\frac{n+1}{2}$ th item in a cumulative frequency distribution. If the variable is discrete, this value can often be read from the table as can be seen in the example of Table 10.7.

For continuous variables it is assumed that the items within a group are evenly spread across the class interval, each item being at the mid-value of a range obtained by dividing the class interval by the frequency within the class. In this case the value of the $\frac{n+1}{2}$ th item is found from the formula:

$$\text{Median value} = \begin{array}{c} \text{value at} \\ \text{beginning of} \\ \text{class interval} \\ \text{containing} \\ \text{median} \end{array} + \dfrac{\begin{array}{c} \text{class} \\ \text{interval} \end{array} \left\{ \dfrac{n}{2} - \begin{array}{c} \text{cumulative} \\ \text{frequency of} \\ \text{earlier groups} \end{array} \right\}}{\begin{array}{c} \text{frequency of class} \\ \text{containing median.} \end{array}}$$

The use of this formula is illustrated in Table 10.8; it shows the calculation of the median for the sample of national servicemen's heights quoted in Table 10.5. An alternative method of determining the median is given in the next chapter.

The mode is the value which occurs most frequently. For discrete variables it can often be read from the table. For example, from the data of Table 10.7 it can be seen that there are more addresses with two electors, than addresses with any other number of electors. The modal number of electors per address is therefore two.

The mode cannot be found exactly for continuous variables. As a first approximation the mid-value of the class interval containing the greatest frequency may be used. For a second approximation the frequencies of the neighbouring classes can be taken into account since the mode is likely to be nearer the larger of these two classes. The following formula may be used:

$$\text{Mode} = \begin{array}{c} \text{value at beginning} \\ \text{of class of} \\ \text{greatest frequency} \end{array} + \dfrac{\begin{array}{c} \text{class interval} \times \text{frequency of next} \\ \text{higher class} \end{array}}{\text{sum of frequencies of adjacent classes}}$$

The application of this formula to the data of Table 10.8 gives the modal height for the sample of national servicemen.

$$\text{Modal height} = 67 + \frac{2 \times 16}{27 + 16} \text{ ins.}$$

$$= 67\cdot74 \text{ inches.}$$

A two-humped distribution will have two modes, though it is sometimes reasonable to regard one of these modes as secondary to the other. The distribution of weekly earnings for men in government industrial establishments, shown in Diagram 10.3. has two modes, both of more or less equal importance. The apparent numerical value of the mode, and in some cases the number of modes, which can be recognized is partly dependent on the way in which the data has been grouped. The distribution of professors' salaries shown in Table 10.3. appears to have only one mode at about £1,450, but there is at least one secondary mode at £2,500 which has been suppressed by the form of grouping used.

The suitability of these three averages for use in any particular problem may be determined by considering the ease with which they may be calculated and interpreted and the shape of the distribution or distributions involved.

For symmetrical distribution all these averages have the same value, for skew distributions they have different values, and the more skew the distribution, the greater the differences between the averages. This fact is illustrated in Diagram 10.5.

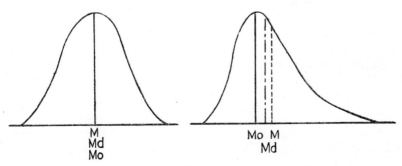

DIAGRAM 10.5 *Averages for Symmetrical and Skew Distributions.*

It is interesting to consider the values of these three averages for the distribution of heights of national servicemen and weekly earnings of men in the paper and printing industries. The results are summarized in Table 10.9. The averages for the heights which form a fairly symmetrical distribution are very similar to each other: those for the less symmetrical earnings distribution differ considerably.

For highly skew distributions, the median and mode are more typical the distribution as a whole, than is the arithmetic mean which is greatly affected by extreme values.

The median is generally easier to calculate than the mean: also its calculation is unaffected by the presence of 'under' and 'over'

TABLE 10.9
AVERAGE HEIGHTS AND AVERAGE EARNINGS

Average	Heights of national servicemen ★	Earnings of men in paper & printing industries
Mean	67·49 ins.	84·25 s.
Median	67·47 ins.	79·45 s.
Mode	67·14 ins.	76·56 s.

groups. The mode is easily found for variables which can only take small whole number values, but in other cases, the calculation of the mode may be unsatisfactory.

The median and mode are very easy averages to interpret: half the values in a frequency distribution are below the median, and half above it: and if there is only one mode, it is the most usual value. The arithmetic mean is not so easily explained, but it is used so frequently that its interpretation presents little practical difficulty. Also this average is to be preferred in all problems involving aggregates, since the product of the arithmetic mean and the number of values gives the sum of the values. In most problems, however, it is desirable to measure both the average and the variation about the average. Further discussion of the use of averages must therefore be left until after consideration of measures of dispersion in the next chapter.

★ These averages have been calculated from the complete data, not from the sample of 100 heights shown in Table 10.5. This has been done to avoid sampling errors.

CHAPTER 11

MEASURES OF DISPERSION

THE simplest measure of dispersion is the range i.e. the difference between the largest and the smallest values. This measure is useful for describing the variation in such things as the ages of pupils in a class or the salaries to be earned in a particular occupation. In practice, however, the range has one very serious disadvantage: its numerical value can be greatly changed by the inclusion or exclusion of one exceptional individual in the group. The age range of a class can be considerably increased by the admission of one child who is much older than the others: the salary range of an occupational group will be greatly reduced if the best paid member is omitted. This difficulty can be overcome by ignoring the extreme values and considering the range of, say, the middle fifty per cent of the frequency only. This range is described as the interquartile range, the quartiles being defined as the items which are one quarter and three quarters along the frequency distribution. Any other convenient fraction might be used instead of one half, though the only alternative which is used frequently in practice is the interdecile range, obtained by excluding the first and last tenths of the frequency distribution.

The quartiles and deciles are obtained by interpolation from the cumulative frequency distribution. The method is the same as that used for the calculation of the median in the last chapter. It is illustrated in Table 11.1 which uses the data already quoted for the average weekly earnings of men in the paper and printing industries. The results are easily interpreted: half the men in these industries earned between 63s.1d and 99s.4d per week: one quarter earned less than 63s. 1d and the other quarter earned more than 99s. 4d.

At the same date, the median and quartile earnings for women in these same industries were 34s.4d, 28s.0d and 39s.7d respectively. Earnings for men were obviously higher than those for women. They were also more variable: the interquartile range (Q_3-Q_1) was only 11s.7d for women's earnings, but was 36s.3d. for men's earnings. The printing industries provided opportunities for overtime and night work which account for the spread of high earnings among the men.

This comparison can also be made graphically using cumulative frequency curves or ogives, providing either that the total frequencies are the same, or that the frequencies are expressed as percentages.

Cumulative frequency curves for the earnings of men and women in the paper and printing industries have been drawn in Diagram 11.1. Owing to the presence of 'under' and 'over' groups in these distributions, it is not possible to complete these curves, nevertheless the important differences are obvious. The curve for women's earnings is well to the left of that for men's earnings, since their average earnings are so much lower. Also this curve is much steeper than the curve for men's earnings, since the latter are much more variable than women's earnings.

TABLE 11.1

CALCULATION OF MEDIAN AND QUARTILES

Weekly earnings s.	Frequency per 1,000	Cumulative frequency	Weekly earnings s.
Under 40	46	46	Under 40
40– 50	61	107	,, 50
50– 60	101	208	,, 60
60– 70	136	344	,, 70 (Q_1)
70– 80	165	509	,, 80 (Md)
80– 90	148	657	,, 90
90–100	100	757	,, 100 (Q_3)
100–110	73	830	,, 110
110–120	48	878	,, 120
120 & over	122	1000	

$$\frac{n}{2} = 500 \qquad Md = 70 + \frac{10\,(500 - 344)}{165}$$

$$= 79\cdot5s. \text{ or } 79s. \ 6d$$

$$\frac{n}{4} = 250 \qquad Q_1 = 60 + \frac{10\,(250 - 208)}{136}$$

$$= 63\cdot1s. \text{ or } 63s. \ 1d.$$

$$\frac{3n}{4} = 750 \qquad Q_3 = 90 + \frac{10\,(750 - 657)}{100}$$

$$= 99\cdot3s. \text{ or } 99s. \ 4d$$

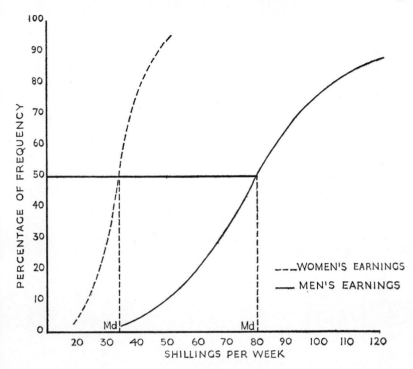

DIAGRAM 11.1 *Earnings of Men and Women in the Paper and Printing Industries,*
1938.

The values of the median and quartiles can be read off from a cumulative frequency curve: they may be taken as corresponding to frequencies, $\frac{n}{2}$, $\frac{n}{4}$, $\frac{3n}{4}$ respectively. The results will not necessarily be identical with those obtained by the calculation of Table 11.1. since the assumptions involved are not quite the same: but the difference in the two sets of estimates is likely to be very small.

Lorenz curves may also be used to compare the variability of two distributions, if the aggregate value of the variable within each class interval is known. The cumulative totals of both frequency and the aggregate values are then expressed as percentages of their respective totals and plotted against each other. If all the values of the variable were the same, half of the total frequency would account for half the aggregate values, three quarters of the total frequency would account for three quarters of the aggregate values, etc. and the Lorenz curve would be a diagonal line. The extent to which any Lorenz curve deviates from this line is a measure of the variability of the distribution which it represents.

This type of curve is frequently used to illustrate variations in income distributions and the size structure of industry. An example is given in Diagram 11.2. which shows the distribution of personal incomes before and after tax in 1954. It provides a measure of the inequality of personal incomes and the levelling effect of taxation.

A very different method of measuring dispersion uses the deviations of all the individuals from the mean. By definition, however,

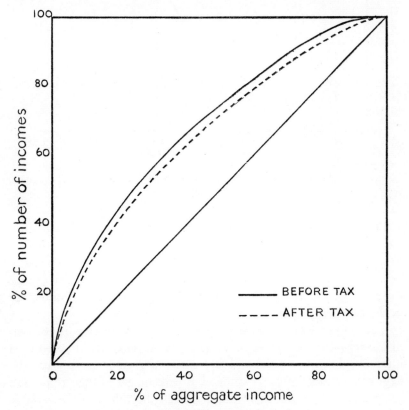

DIAGRAM 11.2   *Distribution of Personal Income before and after Tax. U.K., 1954.*
(For data, see Table 11.2).

TABLE 11.2
DISTRIBUTION OF PERSONAL INCOME BEFORE AND AFTER TAX, U.K. 1954

Range of Income		Number of Incomes	Total of Incomes	Cumulative frequency of Incomes	Cumulative total of Incomes
Over £	not over £	(000's)	(£m)	%	%
Before Tax					
	250	8,540	1,440	32·72	11·81
250	500	8,690	3,280	66·02	38·72
500	750	5,900	3,575	88·62	68·05
750	1,000	1,750	1,475	95·33	80·15
1,000	1,500	700	840	98·01	87·04
1,500	2,000	210	360	98·81	89·99
2,000	3,000	161	388	99·43	93·17
3,000	5,000	96	360	99·80	96·13
5,000	10,000	41	275	99·95	98·38
10,000	20,000	10	128	99·99	99·43
20,000		2	69	100·00	100·00
After Tax					
	250	8,750	1,481	33·52	13·56
250	500	9,420	3,562	69·61	46·18
500	750	5,780	3,489	91·76	78·13
750	1,000	1,315	1,105	96·80	88·25
1,000	2,000	701	926	99·48	96·79
2,000	4,000	127·4	328	99·98	99·23
4,000	6,000	6·41	27·5	99·99	99·98
6,000		0·19	1·5	100·00	100·00

Source of data: National Income and Expenditure Estimates 1955.

the sum of these deviations from the mean is zero, so that it is necessary either to average these deviations without regard to sign, or to average their squares which are all positive. The first alternative gives the mean deviation from the mean, the second alternative gives the variance whose square root is known as the standard deviation. The second alternative produces the more useful formula from a mathematical point of view, consequently it is generally better to use a standard deviation than a mean deviation. The mean deviation from the median is also used as a measure of dispersion, but neither form of mean deviation will be considered here.

The standard deviation is sometimes called the root-mean-square deviation, a name which exactly describes the process by which it is calculated.

Suppose there are n values of X which may be denoted by $X_1 X_2 \ldots X_n$ and that the arithmetic mean of these values is $\bar{X}$. Then the deviations of these values from their mean are $(X_1 - \bar{X})$, $(X_2 - \bar{X})$, $(X_3 - \bar{X}) \ldots (X_n - \bar{X})$: for convenience they may also be written $x_1, x_2, x_3 \ldots x_n$. The standard deviation is usually denoted by σ (sigma) and is given by the formula

$$\sigma = \sqrt{\frac{\Sigma x^2}{n}} \text{ or } \sqrt{\frac{\Sigma (X - \bar{X})^2}{n}}$$

If the mean can be found exactly as in the case of the imaginary data of Table 11.3, this formula can easily be applied. The calculation is similar to that already given for the mean of grouped data, but involves an extra column.

TABLE 11.3

CALCULATION OF STANDARD DEVIATION (1)

X	Frequency	$x = (X - 4)$	fx	fx^2
1	3	-3	-9	27
2	7	-2	-14	28
3	11	-1	-11	11
4	13	0	0	0
5	11	1	$+11$	11
6	7	2	$+14$	28
7	3	3	$+9$	27
Total	55		0	132

Since distribution is symmetrical $\bar{X} = 4$

$$\sigma = \sqrt{\frac{132}{55}}$$

$$= 1.55$$

Generally the mean cannot be determined exactly and the formula must be adapted for use with the original values of X or the values of X measured from some other arbitrary point.

$$no^2 = \Sigma x^2 = \Sigma (X - \bar{X})^2$$
$$= \Sigma (X^2 - 2X\bar{X} + \bar{X}^2)$$
$$= \Sigma X^2 - 2n\bar{X}^2 + n\bar{X}^2$$
$$= \Sigma X^2 - n\bar{X}^2$$
$$\therefore \quad \sigma = \sqrt{\frac{\Sigma X^2}{n} - \bar{X}^2}$$

In Table 11.4 this formula has been applied to the calculation of the standard deviation for the heights of national servicemen quoted in Table 10.5. It is convenient to work in units of the class interval, though these must be converted to the original units at the end of the calculation.

TABLE 11.4

CALCULATION OF STANDARD DEVIATION (2)

Height in ins.	Number of men	Mid Values	(Dev. from 68) ÷ 2 = X	fX	fX²
61–63	4	62	−3	−12	36
63–65	12	64	−2	−24	48
65–67	27	66	−1	−27	27
67–69	32	68	0	0	0
69–71	16	70	1	+16	16
71–73	6	72	2	+12	24
73–75	3	74	3	+ 9	27
Total	100			− 26	+178

$$\sigma = \sqrt{\frac{178}{100} - \left(\frac{26}{100}\right)^2} \quad \text{in working units of 2 ins.}$$
$$= 2\sqrt{1 \cdot 78 - \cdot 0676} \text{ ins.}$$
$$= 2 \cdot 62 \text{ ins.}$$

Direct comparison of the standard deviations of two distributions is only possible if both distributions relate to the same kind of measurement. In other cases a coefficient of variation may be calculated by expressing the standard deviation as a percentage of the mean. This statistic is independent of the units in which the original data are given, and so can be used to compare the variability of any two distributions.

For the heights of national servicemen given in Table 11.4, the coefficient of variation can be found as follows:

$$\text{Coefficient of variation} = \frac{2\cdot62}{67\cdot48} \times 100$$
$$= 3\cdot9\%$$

Weight is a more variable characteristic than height. Similar data for the weights of a sample of national servicemen give a coefficient of variation of 14·0%. (see examples III. 4. and III 5.)

Economic and social data often show much greater variability than natural data. Table 11.5 shows estimates of the average annual incomes for income units classified by the occupation of the head of the unit. An income unit is generally a married couple, or a single person together with their dependents. As might be expected incomes vary more among the self-employed, managerial and retired groups than amongst the manual workers, but even for the latter groups the variability in income is much greater than the variability in either height or weight among national servicemen.

It is often useful to remember that for a normal distribution the effective range is approximately six times the standard deviation. Though few of the distributions to be met with in economic and social statistics are exactly normal, this fact provides a useful check on the calculation of the standard deviation in those cases in which the distribution is single humped and not too skew. For example,

TABLE 11.5

VARIATION IN INCOME

Type of income unit	Mean annual Income £	Standard deviation £	Coefficient of variation per cent
Self-employed	927	1620	175
Managers	1026	1200	117
Clerical & Sales	393	226	58
Skilled manual	430	161	37
Unskilled manual	330	143	43
Retired	180	227	126

Source of data: H. F. Lydall, British Incomes and Savings.
Basil Blackwell 1955

the range is not known exactly for the data of Table 11.4, but may be taken as 61 to 75 inches. One sixth of this range is 2·33 ins. and this value may be compared with the calculated value of the standard deviation of 2·62 ins: in this case the check is satisfactory.

Lastly it is necessary to consider the choice of measures of average and dispersion for use in any problem. It must however be remembered that the various methods described here measure different aspects of variability: consequently they do not necessarily give consistent results in all problems. When quartiles are used, the extreme values are ignored completely: the standard deviation on the other hand, gives considerable weight to the extreme values, since it involves squaring the deviations. Cumulative frequency curves and Lorenz curves illustrate the distribution as a whole.

The formulæ for the mean and standard deviation are more suitable for mathematical treatment than those of the median and quartiles, consequently they are to be preferred in all problems in which the calculation of an average and a measure of dispersion is only the first step of a more extended analysis. On the other hand, for much descriptive work in economic and social statistics the calculation of the median and quartiles or the use of diagrammatic methods is likely to be more satisfactory. Nevertheless it is generally desirable to give the arithmetic mean, as well as the median, since it is possible to combine means obtained from different sources. Also the difference between the arithmetic mean and the median is a useful indication of the skewness of a distribution.

Recommended Reading

Seers, D. 'Income Distributions, 1938 and 1947', Bulletin of the Oxford University Institute of Statistics 1949.

Lydall, H. F. 'The long term trend in the size-distribution of Income', Journal of the Royal Statistical Society, series A (General) 1958.

Knowles, K. G. J. C., and Hill, T. P. 'On the difficulties of measuring wage differentials', Bulletin of the Oxford University Institute of Statistics, 1954.

CHAPTER 12

THE NORMAL DISTRIBUTION

THERE are many theoretical distributions which can be used to give approximate descriptions of observed data and to develop statistical theory: of these, the best known is the normal distribution.

At one time the normal distribution was regarded as an important natural distribution, since many measurements of the physical characteristics of plants and animals appear to be distributed more or less in this way. Today however, it is recognized that skew distributions are just as natural as symmetrical distributions, and the normal distribution is only one of several theoretical distributions which can sometimes be used to describe observed data. Scientists have found the normal distribution useful for the description of the 'errors' which occur in many types of experiment. It is also generally assumed that the variation of intelligence in human populations follows a normal law, and consequently that this distribution is useful for describing the distribution of marks obtained in large scale examinations.

The normal distribution is a uni-modal symmetrical distribution of a continuous variable. Although normal variates have no theoretical limits, extreme values of the variable occur only rarely and almost the whole distribution is concentrated within a relatively narrow range. This distribution may be described by the normal curve, a bell-shaped curve which extends indefinitely in both directions, though the tails of the curve, i.e. the areas between the ends of the curve and the x-axis, are very thin. (see Diagram 12.1)

In the last chapter, it was suggested that the choice of average and measure of dispersion to be used to describe any particular frequency distribution must depend on the shape of the distribution. For the normal distribution the mean and standard deviation are generally chosen, since these parameters provide the constants for the mathematical formula which describes it. If the mean and standard deviation of a normal distribution are known, it is possible to calculate any of its other characteristics, including the proportion of the total

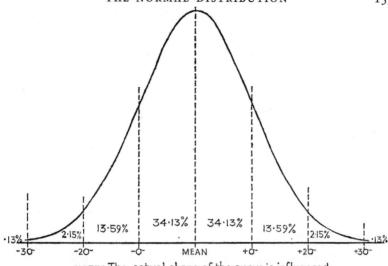

NOTE: The actual shape of the curve is influenced by the scale on which it is drawn.

DIAGRAM 12.1 *The Normal Curve.*

frequency which lies within any particular range of the variable. Also if the variable is expressed in terms of its standard deviation as unit, and measured as deviations from the mean, all normal distributions can be described by the same formula and represented by the same normal curve. This characteristic of the normal distribution is very important since it means that only one table is necessary to show the proportionate frequencies for all distributions of this type. A very simple version of such a table is shown on page 154. *

The information given in this table can be expressed in other ways. From the first and last entries, it is clear that only ·26 per cent of the total frequency lies outside a range of three standard deviation on either side of the mean. In other words, although the theoretical range for a normal variate is infinite, its effective range is only six times its standard deviation. This fact was noted in the last chapter where it was used to check numerical calculations of the standard deviation.

Another useful result which can be derived from the same table is the fact that roughly 95 per cent of the total frequency lies within

* Table 12.1 has been derived from Table 1 of Statistical Tables for Biological, Agricultural and Medical Research by Sir Ronald A. Fisher and Dr Frank Yates, published by Oliver and Boyd, by permission of the authors and publishers.

TABLE 12.1

THE NORMAL DISTRIBUTION

Range of values of x			Proportion of frequency within range
less than		$m - 3\sigma$	·13
$m - 3\sigma$	to	$m - 2\sigma$	2·15
$m - 2\sigma$	to	$m - \sigma$	13·59
$m - \sigma$	to	m	34·13
m	to	$m + \sigma$	34·13
$m + \sigma$	to	$m + 2\sigma$	13·59
$m + 2\sigma$	to	$m + 3\sigma$	2·15
$m + 3\sigma$	and	over	·13
Total			100·00

a range twice the standard deviation on either side of the mean: i.e. within a range, mean ± 2.s.d. If the marks awarded to a large number of candidates taking the same examination are distributed normally about a mean of 50 with a standard deviation of 15, then approximately 2·5 per cent of candidates will have more than 80 marks (mean + 2.s.d.) and another 2·5 per cent of candidates will have less than 20 marks (mean − 2.s.d.). If the heights of the boys in a certain large school form a normal distribution with mean 4 ft. 6 ins. and standard deviation 3 ins.: then approximately 95 per cent of the boys will be taller than 4 ft. but shorter than 5 ft.

These are simple examples, relating to ideal rather than to actual situations. It is true that observed distributions of heights and examination marks are frequently described as approximately normal: but they differ from the theoretical normal distribution in a number of ways. It is therefore necessary to consider the meaning of the phrase "approximately normal".

The observed data relate to a finite, though most probably a large population, whereas the theoretical distribution describes an infinite population. Normal variates are theoretically unlimited in value, but observed heights or marks can only take values within a limited range. Also all normal variables are continuous, but examination marks are generally confined to whole number values and heights may be measured only to the nearest unit. Nevertheless both these types of distribution can approximate to a normal distribution in the sense that the proportions of the total frequency within various ranges of the variable are similar to the corresponding frequencies for the theoretical normal distribution.

Naturally the normal distribution provides a better description of some frequency distributions than others. Diagrams 12.2 and 12.3 show normal curves fitted to histograms of the heights and weights of national servicemen. The distribution of heights approximates more closely to a normal distribution than does the distribution of weights, which is somewhat skew.

The same comparison can be made using Table 12.2. The mean and standard deviation of each distribution has been calculated from the complete data and used to determine the class intervals. The percentage frequencies within these ranges were then read from cumulative frequency curves: they may be compared with the theoretical proportions shown in Table 12.1. Again it is clear that the distribution of heights approximates more closely to a normal distribution than does the distribution of weights.

TABLE 12.2

PERCENTAGE FREQUENCY DISTRIBUTIONS FOR HEIGHTS AND WEIGHTS OF NATIONAL SERVICEMEN

Range	Heights		Weights	
	Range in inches	% frequency	Range in lb.	% frequency
Under $m - 3\sigma$	under 59.6	0·22	under 86.2	0·05
$m - 3\sigma$ to $m - 2\sigma$	59·6–62·3	2·27	86·2–102·7	1·09
$m - 2\sigma$ to $m - \sigma$	62·3–64·9	13·27	102·7–119·2	13·44
$m - \sigma$ to m	64·9–67·5	34·80	119·2–135·7	38·13
m to $m + \sigma$	67·5–70·1	33·76	135·7–152·2	32·81
$m + \sigma$ to $m + 2\sigma$	70·1–72·7	12·99	152·2–168·7	11·13
$m + 2\sigma$ to $m + 3\sigma$	72·7–75·4	2·53	168·7–185·2	2·62
$m + 3\sigma$ and over	75·4 & over	0·16	185·2 & over	0·73
Total		100.00		100.00
Mean	67·5		135·7	
s.d.	2·62		16·5	

Source of data: W. J. Martin The Physique of Young Adult Males, M.R.C. Memo No. 20.

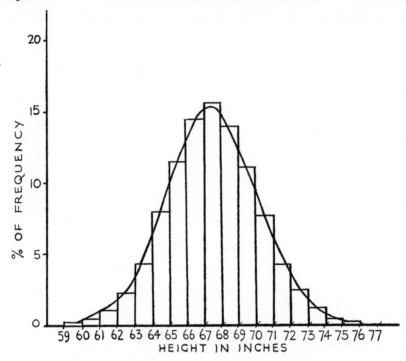

DIAGRAM 12.2   *Distribution of Heights of National Servicemen.*

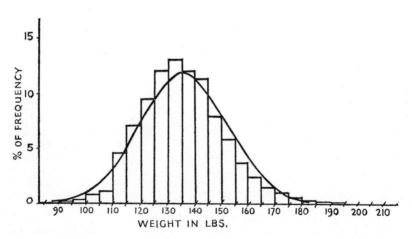

DIAGRAM 12.3   *Distribution of Weights of National Servicemen.*

The shape of a frequency distribution is an important fact concerning the variable which it describes. It can be used to recognize different types of plants and animals. For example, the two races of herrings which are generally found in the North Sea can be distinguished by the frequency distributions for the numbers of their vertebrae. The number varies from 54 to 59 for both races, but the modal number is 56 for one and 57 for the other. Obviously this method is applicable only to shoals of herrings and not to individual fish.

Similar methods of analysis are sometimes applied in cases of disputed authorship. Authors vary considerably in the length of the sentences which they use and the extent to which they vary this length in their writings. For many authors there is a typical frequency distribution of sentence length which could be used to distinguish their writings from the work of others.

Neither of these examples involves normal distributions. When the typical distributions are normal more complicated analyses are possible, since the normal distribution is particularly suitable for mathematical treatment. It will often be possible to separate a multi-modal distribution derived from heterogeneous data for several varieties of plants and animals into the normal distributions appropriate for the individual varieties. Such an analysis can be used to demonstrate the existence of more than one variety and so to assist in the process of classification.

An important example of the use of this method is provided by Karl Pearson's work on the trypanosomes of the tsetse fly. These parasites are the cause of sleeping sickness in cattle and horses in many parts of Africa. They had been the subject of much research work before Karl Pearson became interested in them. In particular, information was available concerning the lengths of trypanosomes obtained from various hosts, but the accepted classification was faulty in many respects. Karl Pearson was able to show that for each distinct species these lengths were distributed normally: by splitting some bi-modal distributions to give two normal distributions he demonstrated that groups that were formerly regarded as homogeneous, actually included two distinct species.

Similar methods have been used to determine the age-distribution of cod in particular fisheries. Cod grow continuously throughout their lives, and the frequency distribution of the lengths of a sample of cod of all ages is multi-modal. If such a distribution is sorted into its component normal distributions, the relative proportions of fish of each age can be determined.

Though the fact that an observed distribution approximates to normal can be of considerable practical importance, it is rarely of any theoretical significance. Nevertheless there are circumstances in which it may be reasonable to deduce the shape of a particular distribution from theoretical considerations. This point is illustrated in the following discussion of income distributions.

Income distributions are known to be highly skew: on the other hand it is generally assumed that intelligence is distributed normally. Now if it can be assumed that income should vary with intelligence, it would be reasonable to expect these characteristics to have distributions of the same shape, and it becomes necessary to explain why this is not so. Several explanations are possible. The social injustice inherent in the present economic system may distort the natural income distribution which is normal. Alternatively one or both of the initial assumptions may be rejected. It may be more reasonable to suppose that income depends on the possession of two or more abilities rather than on a single factor such as intelligence. In this case the assumption that each of these abilities is distributed normally is compatible with the assumption that their combined effect produces a skew income distribution. On the other hand it might not be unreasonable to assume that intelligence has a skew distribution. Since intelligence can only be measured indirectly, the shape of its distribution largely depends on the methods used for its measurement.

The normal distribution is of very considerable importance in the statistical theory of sampling, since it can be used to describe the distribution of the sampling errors which occur in a wide range of problems.

Recommended Reading

Rhodes, E. C. 'The Pareto Distribution of Incomes', *Economica*, 1944.
Roy, A. D. 'The Distribution of Earnings and Individual Output', *Economic Journal*, 1950.

CHAPTER 13

A CORRELATION COEFFICIENT

THE last three chapters have been concerned with the distributions of single variables: it is now necessary to consider problems involving two variables and the relationship, if any, between them. Distributions of heights and weights of men have been discussed separately, but these characteristics are not independent and it would be interesting to consider the way in which height varies with weight or weight varies with height.

There are several ways of analysing the relationship between two sets of measurements, but it is convenient to begin with a graphical method. If many data are available they should be arranged in a two-way frequency table: if only a few pairs of values can be obtained, they can be represented as points on a scatter diagram. The relationship between the variables will be reflected in the arrangement of the frequencies or points: if these tend to be clustered about a diagonal, the variables are said to be correlated. This correlation may be either positive or negative according to whether large values of one variable are associated with large or small values of the other.

Examples are given in Table 13.1. and Diagram 13.1.

Table 13.1. gives an analysis of the lengths and breadths of 232

TABLE 13.1
RELATIONSHIP BETWEEN LENGTH AND
BREADTH OF 232 PRIVET LEAVES

Length in tenths of an inch	Breadth in tenths of an inch								
	2–4	4–6	6–8	8–10	10–12	12–14	14–16	16–18	Total
9–8						1		1	2
8–7					3	5	7	6	21
7–6				5	17	12	13	2	49
6–5			4	17	24	13	1		59
5–4		3	24	21	14				62
4–3		15	15	3					33
3–2	2	2	2						6
Totals	2	20	45	46	58	31	21	9	232

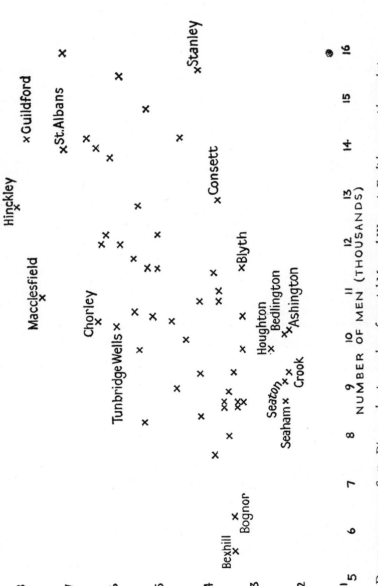

DIAGRAM 13.1   Scatter Diagram showing numbers of occupied Men and Women in English towns with populations
20,000–50,000 in 1951.

Source of data: Census 1951, England and Wales: Occupation Tables.

privet leaves taken from a garden hedge. Privet leaves do not vary greatly in shape, consequently the larger leaves are generally both longer and broader than the smaller leaves and the frequencies tend to cluster about a diagonal.

Diagram 13.1 shows the numbers of occupied men and women for English towns with populations of 20,000 to 50,000 at the 1951 Census. The ratio of men and women who are either employed or self-employed varies very much according to the basic industries of the town. Compared with other districts, the mining towns of Seaham, Ashington, Consett and Stanley had very little employment for women. The seaside resorts of Bexhill and Bognor and the textile towns such as Rawtenstall, Macclesfield and Hinckley and the market towns Tunbridge Wells and St Albans provided employment for a relatively large number of women.

In both these cases there is an obvious relationship between the variables, though this relationship is by no means exact. Both pairs of variables are positively correlated.

In some problems it will be sufficient to illustrate the existence or absence of such an association: in other cases the scatter diagram or two-way table will be used as the first stage of a more comprehensive analysis which may include the calculation of a coefficient to measure the strength of the association. One method of deriving such a correlation coefficient is described below.

Suppose there are n pairs of values of two variables X and Y and that x and y represent the deviations of these variables from their respective means.

$$\text{i.e. } x = X - \bar{X} \text{ and } y = Y - \bar{Y}$$

In Chapter 11 the standard deviation was used as a measure of the variation of a single variable. The square of this standard deviation which is known as the variance is also a measure of variation. The variances of X and Y may be written

$$\text{var } X = \frac{\Sigma x^2}{n} \text{ and var } Y = \frac{\Sigma y^2}{n}$$

These formulae suggest that the quantity $\dfrac{\Sigma xy}{n}$ might be used to measure the way in which X and Y vary together. This quantity is

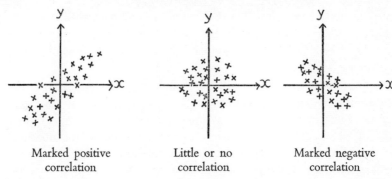

| Marked positive correlation | Little or no correlation | Marked negative correlation |

N.B.   The products xy are positive in the first and third quadrants and negative in the second and fourth quadrants.

DIAGRAM 13.2

known as the covariance of X and Y and the summation is taken over all pairs of values of the variables.

Now if the variables are positively correlated, larger than average values of X will tend to be associated with larger than average values of Y and smaller than average values of X will tend to be associated with smaller than average values of Y. In other words, the deviations of x and y will generally have the same sign and the sum of the products xy will tend to be a relatively large positive quantity. Under these circumstances the covariance is positive. If on the other hand there is no relationship between the variables, x and y are just as likely to have opposite signs as they are to have the same sign: the sum of the products xy and the covariance will tend to be very small. If the variables are negatively correlated, this sum and the covariance will be negative (see Diagram 13.2).

The covariance is certainly a measure of the strength of the correlation, but it is not a very convenient measure, since its numerical value depends on the units in which x and y are measured. To overcome this difficulty, the covariance is divided by the product of the standard deviations of x and y. The quotient which is a number, is known as the product moment correlation coefficient. It is generally denoted by r.

$$\text{i.e. } r = \frac{cov. \; xy}{\sigma_x \, \sigma_y} = \frac{\Sigma xy}{\sqrt{\Sigma x^2 \; \Sigma y^2}}$$

The values of x and y are rarely available in numerical examples. It is therefore convenient to transform this formula for r into one which involves the original values of X and Y or their deviations from some arbitrary point, not the mean.

Now $\Sigma x^2 = \Sigma X^2 - n\bar{X}^2$ and $\Sigma y^2 = \Sigma Y^2 - n\bar{Y}^2$

This result was obtained on page 149

$$\text{Also } \Sigma xy = \Sigma(X - \bar{X})(Y - \bar{Y})$$

$$= \Sigma XY - \bar{X}\Sigma Y - \bar{Y}\Sigma X + n\bar{X}\bar{Y}$$

$$= \Sigma XY - n\bar{X}\bar{Y}$$

$$\text{Hence } r \quad = \frac{\Sigma XY - n\bar{X}\bar{Y}}{\sqrt{(\Sigma X^2 - n\bar{X}^2)(\Sigma Y^2 - n\bar{Y}^2)}}$$

The general arrangement for calculations of the correlation coefficient is similar to that adopted for the standard deviation. An example is given in Table 13.2. The amount of arithmetic required can often be reduced by working in deviations from suitable values of the variables. Also in some cases it is convenient to change one or both variables by dividing by a common factor. Similar methods were used to reduce the amount of arithmetic involved in calculations of the mean and standard deviation.

The interpretation of correlation coefficients presents many difficulties.

Numerically the correlation coefficient cannot be greater than unity. The extreme values $r = +1$ and $r = -1$ occur only when the relationship between the variables is exact and the points of the scatter diagram lie on a straight line. Under these circumstances the correlation is described as perfect. A large fraction is indicative of a stronger correlation than a small fraction but the strength of the correlation is not directly proportional to the numerical value of the coefficient.

If both variables are distributed normally and there is a real relationship between them, r^2 is a more useful measure of the strength of the association than is the value of r itself. Under these conditions, r^2 measures the proportion of the total variation in one variable which

TABLE 13.2

CALCULATION OF A CORRELATION COEFFICIENT

Town	Population (000's)	No. of grocers' shops	Dev. from 26	Dev. from 101			
	X	Y	X	Y	X²	Y²	XY
Eastbourne	58	119	+32	+18	1024	324	+576
Hastings	66	185	+40	+84	1600	7056	+3360
Southport	86	281	+60	+180	3600	32400	+10800
Worthing	68	140	+42	+39	1764	1521	+1638
Bognor	26	64	0	−37	—	1369	—
Folkestone	45	101	+19	0	361	—	—
Kings Lynn	26	80	0	−21	—	441	—
Lowestoft	43	152	+17	+51	289	2601	+867
Paignton	26	49	0	−52	—	2704	—
Redcar	28	74	+ 2	−27	4	729	−54
Weston-s-Mare	40	89	+14	−14	196	144	−168
Whitley Bay	33	79	+ 7	−22	49	484	−154
Totals			+233	+201	8887	49773	16865

$$r = \frac{\Sigma XY - n\overline{X}\,\overline{Y}}{\sqrt{(\Sigma X^2 - n\overline{X}^2)(\Sigma Y^2 - n\overline{Y}^2)}}$$

$$= \frac{16865 - \dfrac{233 \times 201}{12}}{\sqrt{\left(8887 - \dfrac{233^2}{12}\right)\left(49773 - \dfrac{201^2}{12}\right)}}$$

$$= \cdot 91$$

is explained by its relationship with the other. For example, the distributions of heights and weights of adult women shown in Table 13.3 approximate, though not closely, to normal distributions, and the correlation between these variables is $r = + \cdot 34$. In this case $r^2 = \cdot 12$, which suggests that roughly 12 per cent of the variation in the weight of these women can be explained by the variation in their heights.

This method of reasoning suggests that a correlation of ·3 or less which explains less than 10 per cent of the total variation is a weak correlation: a correlation of ·7 which explains about one half of the variation is reasonably effective and a correlation of ·9 or over which

TABLE 13.3

HEIGHT AND WEIGHT OF ADULT WOMEN, 1951

Weight central value in lbs.	Height Central value in inches											Total
	54	56	58	60	62	64	66	68	70	72	74	
281·5	—	—	—	—	—	I	—	—	—	—	—	I
269·5	—	—	—	—	—	I	—	—	—	—	—	I
257·5	—	—	—	—	—	—	I	—	—	—	—	I
245·5	—	—	—	—	I	I	I	—	—	—	—	3
233·5	—	—	—	—	2	—	I	—	I	—	—	4
221·5	—	—	I	—	3	3	I	I	—	—	—	9
209·5	—	—	—	4	3	9	2	I	2	—	—	21
197·5	—	—	4	3	9	9	7	4	I	—	—	37
185·5	—	—	2	12	26	34	21	8	I	3	2	109
173·5	—	—	7	19	35	65	36	24	10	I	2	199
161·5	—	I	11	29	87	90	66	36	14	3	—	337
149·5	—	3	20	66	157	162	140	57	10	3	—	618
137·5	—	I	21	119	196	313	211	95	13	—	—	969
125·5	—	4	53	164	323	407	182	37	4	I	—	1175
113·5	—	8	57	227	349	308	72	12	—	—	—	1033
101·5	3	8	62	146	140	51	9	—	—	—	—	419
89·5	—	7	15	24	9	—	—	—	—	—	—	55
77·5	2	I	I	—	—	—	—	—	—	—	—	4
Total	5	33	254	813	1340	1454	750	275	56	11	4	4995

Source of data: Women's Measurements and Sizes, H.M.S.O., 1957.

explains more than 80 per cent of the variation is a strong correlation. Although few economic or social variables are distributed normally, these results provide a useful guide to the interpretation of numerical results.

The correlation between the crude death-rate and the proportion of the population aged 65 or more for a sample of medium sized English towns is $r = + \cdot 64$ (see Diagram 13.3). In this case $r^2 = \cdot 41$, which suggests that although the proportion of elderly persons is an important factor influencing the crude death rate of towns, it is certainly not the only factor. This conclusion could of course be confirmed by a study of the standardized death rates for these same towns.

In an analysis made for Canada for 1941 it was found that the

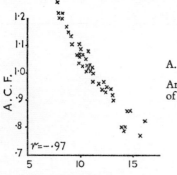

A.

Area Comparability Factor and proportion of population aged 65 years or more.

B.

Crude Death rate and proportion of population aged 65 or more

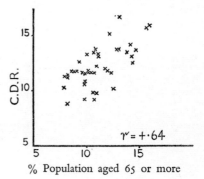

C.

Net movement to work per 1000 population and proportion of retired and occupied males in social classes IV and V.

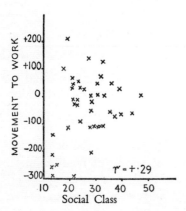

All data relate to group of 42 towns (U.Ds and M.Bs) with populations of 40,000–50,000 at 1951 Census. *Source of data: Census 1951, England and Wales: Registrar Generals' Statistical Review 1951*

DIAGRAM 13.3   *Scatter Diagrams.*

correlation between income and standard of education for 177 male occupational groups was $r = + \cdot 61$.* Income was measured by average remuneration for the group and educational standard by the proportion of men who had had nine years or more of full-time schooling. It is unlikely that either of these distributions is exactly normal, nevertheless it is reasonable to conclude that this is an effective correlation. Generally the educated man has a better chance of engaging in a well paid occupation than the uneducated man, but lack of formal education is not necessarily a handicap from this point of view.

The distribution of town populations is highly skew, and this factor should be taken into account when interpreting the correlation between the number of grocers' shops and the size of the population of seaside resorts which was calculated in Table 13.2. In this case, however, the correlation coefficient is high, $r = + \cdot 91$ and there can be little doubt that the differences in the numbers of grocers' shops to be found in seaside resorts are largely due to differences in the size of their populations.

When interpreting correlation coefficients it is not sufficient to consider their numerical values. These numerical values are essentially measures of the shape of a bivariate frequency distribution or measures of the agreement or disagreement between two sets of numbers. The correlation coefficient can only be used to measure the strength of the relationship between two variables if such a relationship exists. If there is no real relationship between the variables, the correlation is meaningless or nonsense whatever its numerical value.

Examination papers are a fruitful source of nonsense correlations. Here are two examples taken from the Certificate Papers of the Royal Statistical Society. The correlation between the numbers of mentally defective persons registered in this country in the years 1924–37 and the number of wireless licences issued in those same years was $r = + \cdot 98$: that between the annual notifications of deaths from diphtheria and the consumption of beer for the years 1939–47 was $r = - \cdot 82$!

Both these nonsense correlations involve time series with marked

* Charles, Enid: The Changing Size of Family in Canada, Census Monograph No. 1. Edmond Cloutier, Ottawa, 1948.

trends during the periods quoted: and this fact accounts for the high values of the coefficients even though the variables for which they are calculated are unrelated.

Many of the correlations which can be derived from time series, though not wholly nonsense are of little practical value. The correlation between the index of wholesale prices of materials used in the non-food manufacturing industries and the index of retail prices for the twelve months beginning September 1954 was $r = - \cdot47$. In this case it is reasonable to assume a real relationship between the indices. There can be little doubt that changes in the prices of materials must contribute to changes in the prices of goods made from them, though there must be a time lag before the effect of these changes can be fully realised and this time lag will not be the same for all commodities. But the relationship between the indices of wholesale and retail prices cannot be measured by this negative correlation coefficient: a much more complex analysis would be required to deal with this relationship satisfactorily.

In some problems, the correlation coefficient is simply used as a measure of agreement between two sets of numbers. For instance, the correlation between the marks given to the same scripts by different examiners may be used as a measure of the agreement that can be achieved between examiners. These correlations vary considerably between different subjects: it is easier to get agreement on the number of marks to be given to a set of arithmetic exercises than it is to get agreement on the number of marks to be given to an English essay.

The first scatter diagram of Diagram 13.3 shows the relationship between the Area Comparability Factor (see page 75) and the proportion of the population aged 65 or more for 42 medium sized English towns. Both these series measure an aspect of the age distribution of a population which influences mortality rates: consequently there is a very strong correlation between them.

Two other problems of interpretation should be mentioned though the techniques required for their analysis are beyond the scope of this book.

Most though not all of the correlation coefficients discussed in this chapter have been calculated for large groups. It should be noted, however, that since the correlation coefficient is liable to relatively large sampling errors, weak correlations obtained from relatively few data rarely justify important conclusions.

In relatively few problems is it possible to isolate two factors and consider the relationship between them without reference to other factors which influence them both. For example, a survey of household expenditure made in 1932* showed that there was a positive correlation between expenditure on meat and expenditure on bread of $r = + \cdot 23$. Further analysis of the data however revealed that this correlation was due to the fact that expenditure on meat and expenditure on bread both increased with increases in income. At any particular income level, expenditure on bread and meat were alternatives: if therefore the effect of income changes were ignored, the correlation between expenditure on meat and bread was negative $r = - \cdot 18$. The possibility that an observed correlation may be explained by the presence of a third factor which has not been included in the analysis should always be considered.

* Allen R. G. D. and Bowley A. L. *Family Expenditure*, George Allen & Unwin, 1935.

Recommended Reading

Wilkins, L. T. 'Estimation of the Social Class of Towns', *Applied Statistics* Vol 1., 1951.
Women's Measurements and Sizes, H.M.S.O., 1957.
Houldsworth, Sir Hubert. The Pits of Britain, *Transactions of the Manchester Statistical Society*, 1952–3.

III.   1.

Distributions of sentence length obtained from three daily newspapers

Number of words per sentence	Number of sentences A	B	C
0– 4	4	1	4
5– 9	15	11	13
10–14	14	13	22
15–19	30	15	23
20–24	24	17	27
25–29	20	28	17
30–34	8	11	10
35–39	1	7	3
40–44	4	8	–
45–49	–	2	1
50–54	–	5	–
55–59	–	–	–
60–64	–	1	–
65–69	–	1	–
70–74	–	–	–
Total	120	120	120

Draw histograms to illustrate these distributions. Two of these distributions were obtained from popular dailies, the other from a more serious newspaper.

III.   2.   Use the data of Exercise I. 2 to draw cumulative frequency curves for the age distributions of migrants to Corby and Worthing.

For each town estimate

(i)   The proportion of migrants in the age-group 15–45 years.

(ii)   The median age of the migrants.

III. 3. Use the data of Table 13.3 to answer the following questions.

(i) How many women who were less than 4 ft. 11 ins. tall weighed at least 143½ lb.?

(ii) What was the average weight of women whose heights were 5 ft. 9. ins. or more?

III. 4. Calculate the mean and standard deviation for the weights of the following sample of 100 National Servicemen.

Wt. in lbs.	No. of Men
100–110	7
110–120	12
120–130	20
130–140	25
140–150	20
150–160	6
160–170	5
170–180	2
180–190	1
190–200	1
200–210	1
Total	100

III. 5. Data from Women's Measurements and Sizes:

	Mean	s. d.
Stature	63·02 ins.	2·59 ins.
Weight	132·81 lb.	22·45 lb.

Calculate the coefficient of variation for each of these measurements. Compare these results with those quoted for National Servicemen in Chapter 11.

III.   6.   *Distribution of prices of sheep sold at an auction sale*

Price in shillings per head	Number of lots
112–130	2
132–150	5
152–160	10
162–170	15
172–180	27
182–190	30
192–200	36
202–210	37
212–220	21
222–230	16
232–240	11
242–260	5
Total	215

Source: Duncan D. C. Statistics of an Auction Sale, Applied Statistics, 1958.

At this sale 14,319 half-bred ewe lambs were sold in 215
lots of approximately 50 and 100 sheep. All bids were made
in units of 2s., and buyers showed a preference for stopping
bidding at the round pound. Calculate the arithmetic mean
price paid for the sheep.

The correct estimate, made from the complete data is
197s., If your estimate differs from this, can you explain the
difference?

III.   7.   Draw Lorenz Curves to illustrate the following information
from the Census of Distribution, 1950.

Establishments with sales	Grocers		Clothing Group	
	No. of Establishments	Sales £000	No. of Establishments	Sales £000
Under £1,000	4,861	2,876	19,761	8,475
£1,000 – £2,500	14,113	25,021	16,480	27,791
£2,500 – £5,000	21,662	79,887	16,172	58,520
£5,000 – £10,000	26,576	190,041	15,588	111,906
£10,000 – £25,000	20,781	314,841	14,310	221,004
£25,000 – £50,000	5,447	183,538	4,368	148,816
£50,000 – £100,000	1,330	87,352	1,531	104,804
£100,000 – £250,000	182	23,397	620	91,877
£250,000 and over	13	4,990	216	111,985
Totals	94,965	911,942	89,046	885,178

Comment on the size distribution of establishments in these retail groups.

III. 8. Draw a scatter diagram to illustrate the relation between the number of enrolments (X) and the percentage attendance (Y) for 30 adult education classes held in Leicester.
Do these statistics provide any evidence to support the opinion that members of small classes attend better than members of large classes?

X	Y	X	Y	X	Y
14	70·4	13	67·7	10	74·3
22	67·5	25	60·5	12	70·0
12	67·0	22	61·0	27	73·0
24	74·8	15	77·2	9	74·4
12	76·0	15	75·2	11	67·9
14	79·3	12	61·8	32	78·9
17	74·7	15	82·5	33	80·9
10	83·8	44	77·1	16	66·7
31	75·9	16	70·3	18	66·7
8	74·4	28	76·5	16	70·5

Source of data: Report of the Department of Adult Education, University of Leicester, 1956-7.

III. 9. Calculate the correlation coefficient between the marks awarded by two examining boards to 16 candidates in an oral examination.

Candidate	Board I	Board II	Candidate	Board I	Board II
1	120	212	9	230	220
2	260	190	10	210	235
3	130	175	11	210	236
4	230	255	12	230	232
5	210	232	13	120	177
6	180	250	14	210	247
7	200	270	15	220	193
8	240	224	16	170	175

Source of data: Hartog, Sir Phillip J. and Rhodes, E. C.
An Examination of Examinations. Macmillan, 1936.

III.   10.

	1950	1951	1952	1953	1954	1955	1956	1957	1958
X (000's)	3·8	3·9	4·1	4·3	4·6	5·0	6·0	7·1	7·9
Y (000's)	224	228	238	248	260	271	279	292	328

Show that the correlation coefficient between X and Y is + ·97. Discuss the interpretation of this coefficient, given that X is the number of persons found guilty of violence against the person and Y is the number of children aged 15 or over attending grant-aided schools. Both sets of data relate to England and Wales and have been taken from the Annual Abstract 1959.

III.   11. How would you interpret the following product-moment correlation coefficients?

(a) The correlation coefficient between the ages of husbands and wives at marriage for those couples who were married in England and Wales in 1951 was $r = + ·85$.

(b) The correlation between the height of father and height of son for a large sample of fathers and sons was found to be $r = + ·51$.[*]

(c) The correlation between total personal expenditure in the United Kingdom on fuel and light and on travel for the twelve quarters of 1945–7 was $r = - ·54$.

(d) The correlation between the net movement to work into the town per 1,000 population and the proportion of retired and occupied males in social classes IV and V for 42 medium sized towns was $y = + ·29$ (see Diagram 13.3).

(e) The correlation between the average hourly earnings for fitters and labourers employed on time work by 1,947 engineering firms was found to be $r = + ·47$.[**]

[*] Pearson, K. and Lee, A. On the Laws of Inheritance in Man. Biometrika, 1903, No. 2.

[**] Hill, T. P. and Knowles, K. G. J. C. The Variability of Engineering Earnings, Bulletin of the Oxford University Institute of Statistics 1956.

PART IV

CONCLUSION

CHAPTER 14

STATISTICS AND SOCIAL SCIENCE

IT was suggested in the first chapter that the primary purpose of social statistics is the measurement of social phenomena. Some of the measurements used in the social sciences involve only counting or measuring in terms of a well defined unit. The population of a town and the size of a household consist of a number of persons: the value of an income or the price of a commodity can be measured in pounds, shillings and pence. Nevertheless these measurements are not necessarily simple, since the terms town, household, income and price must be defined in administrative, economic or sociological terms. Other measurements are more complex since they involve the use of statistical methods such as averages and index numbers. Such measurements can only be meaningful if the statistical methods have been suitably chosen and the variables used for their calculation suitably defined. In practice of course, the definitions used for the collection of statistics and the methods used in their analysis will change with changing economic and social conditions and with developments in the social sciences.

Many examples could be given to illustrate these changes, but only a few will be mentioned here.

Since Charles Booth made his survey of London Life and Labour towards the end of the last century there have been a number of surveys designed to measure the nature and extent of poverty. Obviously the choice of a definition of poverty must affect the conclusion to be drawn from a survey: the lower the poverty line is set, the fewer the people who will be found living below it. There can however be no absolute standard of poverty: at any point of time or place, the poverty line must be related to the general standard or level of living of the population.

The makers of most of these surveys have defined poverty using the methods introduced by Seebohm Rowntree in his first survey of York in 1899: but this does not mean that they have necessarily used the same poverty line.

Rowntree approached the problem scientifically. He estimated the minimum cost of providing the essential food, shelter, clothing and warmth for each family and compared this cost with the income at its disposal. Families whose incomes were inadequate to purchase these minimum needs were obviously living in poverty.

Scientific methods are most easily applied to food requirements since there is a science of nutrition, but ideas concerning a suitable minimum diet have changed very much since 1899. The diet used by Rowntree to estimate the minimum cost of food for his first survey consisted mainly of bread, cheese and porridge: it made no allowance for butchers' meat though some boiled bacon was allowed since this was cheaper. All later surveys have treated some butchers' meat as a necessity and today a much more varied diet would be regarded as essential.

It has generally been assumed that families living at or near the poverty line could not find cheaper living accommodation even if they wished to do so: the actual rent paid has therefore been accepted as a minimum cost. Rowntree deducted the rent paid by each household from their total earnings before comparing the latter with the estimated minimum cost of the other necessities. After the introduction of compulsory unemployment and health insurance, it was necessary to regard employees' contributions to these funds as inescapable costs to be treated in the same way as rent.

The changes that have taken place in economic and social conditions in this century have made it inevitable that the poverty standard which was used at the beginning of the century should have been modified in these and other ways.

The measurement of overcrowding presents similar problems: as housing conditions improve, higher standards of accommodation are accepted as both desirable and necessary.

During the inter-war years, the Registrar-General used standardized death rates to measure changes in the mortality experience of England and Wales. The census population of 1901 was used as standard, and since this was a very young population, this method of comparison gave very considerable weight to reductions in mortality rates at young ages. In 1941 these standardized rates were replaced by comparative mortality indices, which gave more weight to changes in mortality at older ages and so provided a means of comparison more appropriate to the changed demographic situation.

The measurements used in any science depend not only on the type of phenomena to be described, but also upon the theories which are currently used to describe and explain them. The importance of changing economic theories for the construction of the Retail Price Index was discussed in Chapter 7. Wholesale price indices have also been affected by changes in economic theory.

The first price index to be published regularly in this country was begun by *The Economist* in 1864. Some years later in 1886, the Sauerbeck index was published in the *Journal of the Statistical Society* (now the Royal Statistical Society), and this index was calculated back to 1846. Both indices were simple arithmetic mean indices calculated from the prices of a relatively small number of commodities, mainly raw materials. The Board of Trade published its first wholesale price index in 1903. This was also an arithmetic mean index, but it differed from the others in that it used average values of imports and exports instead of price series for a majority of the commodities.

All three indices were designed to measure changes in the general level of prices and so to measure changes in the purchasing power of money. Economists realized that all prices do not change in the same direction or to the same extent in any period of time, but they were more interested in measuring the extent to which prices moved together than in analysing the differences between individual price movements.

During the period of post-war inflation 1918–1920, the various wholesale price indices gave different estimates of the rate of change in the purchasing power of money. Since the theory of a general level of prices whose changes could be measured by the right kind of price index was still acceptable, this lack of agreement was attributed to defects in the construction of the indices.

The Board of Trade introduced a new index of wholesale prices in 1921 and *The Economist* index was revised in 1928. Several changes were made in both indices, only one of which will be noted here. Both the new indices used the geometric mean instead of the arithmetic mean, since this type of average was more appropriate for current economic theory.

The geometric mean is obtained by taking the nth root of the product of n quantities. It is always less than or equal to the arithmetic mean of the same quantities.* Its use for the construction of a price index tends to minimise the effect of increases in price. This is important since purchasers often choose to buy more of those goods whose prices have risen less than average and such actions have the same effect.

The geometric mean also satisfies the time reversal test but the arithmetic mean does not. The nature of this test can readily be understood by considering an index formed from two price relatives, one of which doubled and the other halved in the same period. The geometric mean of these price relatives will indicate no change in the price level whether the beginning or end of the period is used as base date; but the arithmetic mean shows either a rise or fall according

TABLE 14.1
TIME REVERSAL TEST

Commodity	Year I	Year II	Year I	Year II
A	100	50	200	100
B	100	200	50	100
G.M.	100	100	100	100
A.M.	100	125	125	100

to whether the index is calculated forward from the base date or forward to the base date. This calculation is shown in Table 14.1. It is obviously desirable that an index designed to measure changes in the general level of prices should satisfy this test.

The Board of Trade revised its wholesale price index again in

---

* $\text{G.M.} = \sqrt[n]{x_1, x_2, x_3, \ldots x_n}$

If only two quantities are involved

$\text{G.M.} = \sqrt{x_1 x_2}$

and $(x_1 + x_2)^2 = (x_1 - x_2)^2 + 4x_1 x_2$

$\therefore (x_1 + x_2)^2 \geqslant 4x_1 x_2$

$\therefore \dfrac{x_1 + x_2}{2} \geqslant \sqrt{x_1 x_2}$

or $A.M. \geqslant G.M.$

1951. By this time, economic theory had changed and developed: the concept of a general level of prices was no longer acceptable. Economists were now interested in analysing the price movements for different types of commodities, and determining the relationships, if any, between them. Also it was now thought that the prices of commodities are meaningless without some information concerning the amounts of these commodities which are bought and sold. Since both purchases and prices will change in any given period of time, it is only reasonable to suppose that price changes may have a different significance if viewed forward or backward in time. Under these circumstances, the time reversal test is no longer relevant. In 1951 the geometric mean wholesale price index was replaced by a series of price indices each of which was calculated as a weighted arithmetic mean. The weights were derived from the Census of Production and price indices calculated for the materials used in various important sectors of industry as well as in manufacturing industry as a whole: other price indices were calculated for the products of these industries and for goods sold at home and abroad.

The Board of Trade also publish a large number of commodity price indices from which business executives and others can construct their own price indices using weighting systems derived from a study of their own problems.

The modern study of social statistics is both more complex and more useful than the Political Arithmetic from which it has developed. Social scientists not only use statistics to measure and describe social phenomena. Statistical methods, particularly sampling methods, are needed for the collection of numerical data. Statistical inference is used to test hypotheses and statistics generally are required to demonstrate economic and sociological theories. These other uses of statistics cannot be considered here. Descriptive Statistics must be limited to elementary problems of measurement, even so it should prove a useful introduction to a more general study of this subject.

September 1961

RECOMMENDED READING

Statistics for Government. P. E. P. Planning, Vol. XXIII, No. 406, 28 January 1957.

Stafford, J. 'Wholesale Prices'. J. R. S. S. Series A. General. 1951.

Glass, D. V. 'The Application of Social Research', *British Journal of Sociology*, Vol. 1, 1950.

Government Statistical Services. H.M.S.O.

Stone, R. The Role of Measurement in Economics. University of Cambridge Department of Applied Economics. Monograph 3. Cambridge University Press. 1957.

P. E. P. Poverty: Ten Years After Beveridge. Planning Vol. XIX No. 344, August 1952.

Briggs. A. Seebohm Rowntree. Longmans. 1961.

TEXT-BOOKS FOR FURTHER STUDY

Illersic, A. R. *Statistics and their Application to Commerce*, H. F. L. 1958.

Allen, R. G. D. *Statistics for Economists*, Hutchinson's University Library 1949.

Hill. A. Bradford. *Principles of Medical Statistics*, The Lancet. 1950 (5th Ed.)

Freund, J. E. and Williams, F. J. *Modern Business Statistics*, Pitman 1959.

Mills, F. C. *Statistical Methods*, Pitman, 1955.

Quenouille, M. H. *Associated Measurements*, Butterworth, 1952.

Marris, R. *Economic Arithmetic*, Macmillan 1958.

Blyth, C. *The Use of Economic Statistics*, George Allen & Unwin, 1960.

Devons, E. *British Economic Statistics*, Cambridge University Press, 1956.

Moser, C. A. *Survey Methods in Social Investigation*, Heinemann, 1958

Croxton, F. E., and Cowden, D. J. *General Applied Statistics*, Prentice-Hall, 1948.

Yule, G. U. and Kendall, M. G. *Introduction to the Theory of Statistics*, Griffin & Co., 1950.

As explained in the text, different methods of calculation frequently involve different assumptions and may lead to slightly different numerical results. The following notes are intended to help readers solve their problems, not to present them with 'correct answers' or complete solutions.

I. 1. (a) This comparison should be made between success rates, not between numbers of successes.

   (b) In Wales, as in England, the majority of people live in urban areas. The percentages quoted here have been calculated on very different bases. The numbers of Welsh speaking persons living in urban and rural areas in 1951 were 347,000 and 326,000 respectively.

   (c) There is no figure with which to compare the 793 successes: by it self it cannot be used as a measure of the success of the school.

I. 2. Population pyramids are the most useful form of diagram for this type of problem.

I. 3. The following percentages may be calculated.

   (i) Occupied population as a percentage of total population.

   (ii) Occupied men, women as a percentage of occupied population.

   (iii) Numbers employed in the four industry groups as percentages of occupied population.

I. 4. Absolute scales can be used to show the relative importance of these three types of school as employers of graduate men teachers. Logarithmic scales can be used to illustrate the rate of increase in the number of these teachers employed in each type of school.

I. 6. (a) The 97 per cent and 39 per cent quoted in this question are percentages of very different totals: they cannot therefore be added together and averaged. It is only possible to calculate the proportion of secondary school girls who do homework if either the numbers or proportions of girls in these two types of school are known.

   (b) The chances of leaving the institutions alive are more likely to be proportional to 96·7 % and 93·4 % respectively! But there are many other factors, not mentioned here, which should be taken into account.

II. 1. (a) It is not possible to draw firm conclusions about individual earnings from information concerning the average earnings for groups. It is quite likely that Mr Smith earns more than Mr Brown, though it is not possible to make any estimate of how much more he is likely to earn: on the other hand it is possible, though unlikely, that Mr Brown earns more than Mr Smith.

(b) A reduction in the weight assigned to a particular commodity in the Retail Price Index indicates a reduction in the proportion of total expenditure allocated to this commodity in the average household budget. If total expenditure is increasing, as it was in the period June 1947–January 1956, a reduction in the proportion of total expenditure allocated to any commodity is consistent with an increase in the amount spent upon it.

It should be remembered that the weights for the Interim Index of Retail Prices were derived from the results of a budget inquiry made in 1937–38, adjusted to allow for price changes between that year and June 1947.

II. 2. Index of food prices Jan. 1958 (Jan. 1956 = 100) = 105.

The term vegetarian can be defined in several ways, consequently there is no unique answer to the second part of this question. Here are two possible solutions: the second is probably more useful than the first.

(i) Index all foods except meat, bacon and fish   = 107
(ii) Ditto but with extra weight given to fruit and vegetables = 114

II. 3. Price Index for imported bulbs, 1957 (1954 = 100) = 111 (Laspeyre)
or 111 (Paasche)

II. 4.

Year	Price Indices (Paasche)			Volume Indices (Laspeyre)		
	Bread and cereals	Meat and bacon	Fruit and vegetables	Bread and cereals	Meat and bacon	Fruit and vegetables
1950	83	66	85	113	94	92
1952	95	95	94	113	84	93
1954	100	100	100	100	100	100
1956	109	114	114	99	110	104
1958	121	117	124	99	112	108

II. 5. Index weekly wage rates Jan. 1958 (June 1947 = 100) = 175·1.

II. 6. Average allowance for 1st year schools at 1st year rates = £202·6.
  ,,   ,,   ,, 1st ,,   ,,   ,, 2nd ,,   ,, = £320·3.
  ,,   ,,   ,, 2nd ,,   ,,   ,, 2nd ,,   ,, = £361·2.

∴. % increase in allowances due to change in rates   = 58 %
and % ,,   ,,   ,,   ,, ,,   ,,   ,, size of schools = 13 %

N.B. It is important to remember that in the second year the increased allowances must be paid for a different set of schools.

∴. 58 + 13 ≠ 78

but 158 % of 113 % ≃ 178 %

II. 7. (a) The populations of New Towns include a higher than average proportion of young adults, and this fact certainly helps to explain their
higher than average birth-rates. The suggestion made here concerning
the preference of English people for larger families may or may not
be correct: it cannot be proved by quoting crude birth-rates.

(b) These statements are not necessarily incompatible. Death-rates for each
age group are higher in Japan than in Sweden, even though the crude
death rate for Japan is lower than that for Sweden. Japan has a very
young population.

II. 8.   *Estimate of Seasonal Variation*

J.	—29	A.	+ 3	J.	+23	O.	+ 1
F.	—26	M.	+16	A.	+20	N.	—12
M.	— 7	J.	+21	S.	+ 8	D.	—18

II. 10.   *Estimate of seasonal variation (thousands)*

Quarters	1	2	3	4
	—4·5	+11·2	+4·8	—11·5

Consideration of the quarterly data and/or a graph of this series shows that
estimates of seasonal variation obtained from data for the years 1952–55
cannot be used to obtain a seasonally corrected series for either 1956 or
1957. The number of new registrations was much lower in 1956 than
could have been expected if the trend of the earlier years had continued:
also registrations were exceptionally heavy in the first quarter of 1957
giving a value above the trend instead of below it.

III. 2. Corby   (i) 67 %   (ii) 27 yrs.
Worthing   (i) 41 %   (ii) 39 yrs.

III. 3. (i) 49   (ii) 159·5 lb.

III. 4. $m = 135·8$ lb. $s = 19·0$ lb.

III. 5.   *Coefficients of Variation*

	Men	Women
Stature	3·9 %	4·1 %
Weight	14·0 %	16.9 %

For these groups of men and women there is little or no difference in the
variability of their heights: but weight appears to be a more variable
characteristic among the women than among the men.

Two other points are worth noting. Since the coefficients of variation
for men have been calculated from samples of 100 they may be liable
to considerable sampling errors: the corresponding coefficients calculated
from the complete data are 3·9 % and 12·2 % respectively. The men
belong to a narrower age-range than the women in these groups.

III. 7. In both these groups of retail establishments there are more very small shops than very large shops, but the variation in size is greater among the clothing group than the grocery group. In the former group more than 20 per cent of shops account for less than 1 per cent of total sales, whereas at the other end of the scale, approximately 1 per cent of shops account for roughly 25 per cent of sales.

     The Lorenz curve for the clothing group is well outside that for the grocery group.

III. 8. The scatter diagram cannot be used to support this opinion. ($r = + \cdot 16$)

III. 9. In this example it will be convenient to divide the marks of the first Board by 10, and then to work in deviations from arbitrary values such as 21 and 190. Tables of squares and square roots are very useful for these calculations.

     $r = + \cdot 41$. This is a fairly low correlation suggesting a considerable amount of disagreement between the Boards.

III. 10. Nonsense correlation.

III. 11. (a) $r = + \cdot 85$ is a high correlation, and is a measure of the tendency for men and women to marry persons of similar age to themselves.

    (b) $r^2 = \cdot 26$ and the distributions are approximately normal: this correlation coefficient suggests that one quarter of the variation in the heights of sons can be explained by the variation in the heights of their fathers.

    (c) Both these time series are subject to considerable seasonal variation: but whereas expenditure on fuel and light is highest in the winter quarters, that on travel is highest in the summer. The correlation coefficient is a reflection of these facts.

    (d) This is a rather low positive correlation. It suggests that there is little relationship between the extent to which a town is a workplace or dormitory, and the social class of its population.

    (c) A high correlation between average hourly earnings of fitters and labourers employed by the same firms would indicate a fairly uniform skill differential. In this case $r = + \cdot 47$ which is a rather weak correlation: it suggests considerable diversity between firms in the relationship between the average hourly earnings of these two types of worker.